PLANT LIFE

a
SCIENTIFIC
AMERICAN
book

SIMON AND SCHUSTER · **NEW YORK**

TABLE OF CONTENTS

Growth and other life processes in plants are regulated by comparatively simple but multipotent substances. The best known of these plant hormones are the auxins. The concentration of auxin in plant tissues, varying with the changing length of the day, times the flowering of certain plants. The auxin balance also controls the putting-out and the dropping of leaves. Recently, the discovery of other growth substances has complicated the picture of plant physiology. Along with the auxins, these promise to be powerful agents for use in field and garden.

2. AGROCLIMATOLOGY

The physiology of plants, discussed in the foregoing section, is intimately tied to the changing length of the day, the temperature-swing between day and night, the timing and the volume of rainfall, and other aspects of climate. A new understanding of this interrelationship is now leading to wiser matching and adaptation of field and garden plants to the range of the earth's environments.

3. GROWTH AND FORM

Mushrooms grow in two stages: the first, embryonic; the second, hydraulic. The changing shape of its leaves is a key to the physiological age of a plant. The tissues of plants cultured in laboratory glassware make useful subjects for the study of normal and abnormal growth.

4. GREEN LEAVES AND RED

Photosynthesis, the process by which green leaves synthesize carbohydrates from air and water, is slowly giving up its mystery to persistent and ingenious investigators. Less famous and even less well understood is the process by which leaves fashion the benzene ring, the parent structure of such aromatic compounds as the red pigment of autumn leaves and the dyestuffs of our chemical industry.

5. PLANT DYNAMICS

In addition to the movement of growth, plants have motility of other kinds; they can turn their leaves toward the sun, open and close the petals of their flowers and even catch animals. In pumping large quantities of water high above the ground, trees employ physical principles not found in other pumps and take advantage of the high tensile strength of water.

6. EVOLUTION AND THE PLANT COMMUNITY

Evolution is a communal process; living things adapt to one another in creating the environment in which one and all evolve. Certain unrelated species of trees (or are they vines?) in various jungles of the world strangle other trees and take their place in the sun. The explosion of Mont Pelée extinguished every spark of life on Krakatoa. Soon after the dust cleared away, however, plants began to populate the island again, recapitulating for botanists the process by which the jungles of the Pacific islands were established in aeons past. In the desert, plants have evolved various adaptations to the harshness of nature: they grow less and thus share the water; their seeds survive for years without germinating until just the right amount of rain falls at just the right time; some larger plants poison the soil for yards around and thereby monopolize the local water supply. Animals, as well as plants, contribute to the environment in which plants evolve; flowers are variously adapted to promote their pollination by insects, birds and mammals.

7. APPLIED GENETICS

Two of the three great cereal plants of mankind demonstrate the power of man as an agent of evolution. The wild ancestor of wheat is not yet identified for sure; corn bears no resemblance at all to its two ancestor plants. Now, with the science of genetics at its command, agriculture is breeding new strains to fit specifications drawn in advance.

INTRODUCTION

This is a book about plants that has direct relevance to people. We are obligatory parasites on the plant life of our planet. Plants have the unique faculty of being able to synthesize life substances from raw elements contained in air and water. They thus establish the first link in the chain of life upon which the existence of all other living things depends. Since it follows that plants and people must be made of the same stuff, the study of plant life ultimately can tell us much about ourselves.

The modern botanist is interested in plants as a way to get at questions of life in general. Plants furnish him with cheap and convenient laboratory subjects for investigating growth and form, genetics and evolution and the underlying chemistry of life processes. The reader will also sense throughout this book the lively concern of its authors with the revolutionary implications of their work in the practical realm of agriculture and human nutrition.

The authors are scientists closely associated with the work they report. They wrote the chapters of this book originally as magazine articles, addressed to the 170,000 subscribers and newsstand buyers who make up the diverse audience of Scientific American. Each chapter is thus a self-contained discussion of its topic. Brought together in this book, however, they gain in relevance from one another and present a comprehensive view of the major lines of work in botany today.

The first section of the book deals with the topic of plant hormones, the regulators of plant life processes. Comparatively simple substances, much simpler than hormones in animals, they seem also to be more versatile in function. The same or closely similar substances, the auxins, direct the differentiation of tissues, promote and inhibit growth, and time the opening of flowers, the dropping of leaves and the ripening of fruit. Other plant-growth regulators, different from the auxins in chemistry and in function, have recently been discovered in coconuts and horse chestnuts, in potatoes, carrots and immature bananas, and even in animal tissues. Investigators sense that the near future will see major advances in our understanding of the forces that organize cells in tissues and make tissues form the characteristic structures of their plant species. Meanwhile the new substances portend another cycle of chemical revolution in agriculture. Auxins have already assumed a major role in the technology of farm and garden. The deleafing of cotton plants, for example, makes the mechanical boll-picker feasible, and the spray gun has replaced the hoe in suburbia's unending campaign against chickweed and burdock.

With this background in plant hormones, the reader will be prepared to appreciate the interconnection between climate and plant growth which is the subject of Section 2. The work described here is the harvest of the first decade's experience with the "phytotron." This is a many-roomed greenhouse in which the entire range of the earth's climates may be established at will. Such control of the variable of climate makes it possible to conduct and to expedite many significant lines of research. It has also laid the foundations for the important new applied science of agroclimatology, the matching and adaptation of plants to the regions where they will grow best.

The three chapters in Section 3 suggest the kind of questions that the growth substances are helping to answer. We can now see how it is that mushrooms pop up overnight; we want to know next how the dividing and differentiating cells of the young plant can "tell" that they have formed a complete mushroom, ready for popping. It is clear that plants put out differently shaped leaves at the beginning and end of their growth, but we do not yet have a biochemical explanation of the process of aging. When a small enough snippet of plant tissue is cultured in laboratory glassware, it will not give rise to root and shoot but will proliferate as an inchoate mass of cells. Such cultures resemble plant cancers and so are useful for investigating fundamental questions of growth.

The green and red colors of leaves, with which the next two chapters are concerned, hold the key to the two great chemical processes that plants perform for all of the rest of nature. The green of chlorophyll is designed to absorb just the right wave lengths of sunlight and thus provide the precise quanta of energy needed to achieve the bonding of hydrogen to carbon atoms. This bond is the foundation of all biological and organic chemistry. The red of autumn leaves bespeaks another feat not duplicated in the laboratory. The key structure in the red pigment is the benzene ring, one of the great parent compounds in organic chemistry. It is synthesized in the leaf by some subtle transformation of the sugars that are the first product of photosynthesis. The family of benzene compounds includes the dyestuff industry as well as the colors of autumn and a whole pharmacopoeia of functionally critical chemicals such as morphine, strychnine and quinine. It includes also the natural plastic lignin that bonds the cellulose fibers in the structure of plants and, in the fossil form of coal tar, supplies human chemists with phenol to make an important family of synthetic plastics.

Plants have mechanical and physical as well as chemical interest. A Douglas fir is a waterworks that pumps hundreds of gallons of water hundreds of feet above ground in the course of a day. The explanation for this prowess lies in processes conducted on the microscopic scale in the living cell. Such processes also endow plants with a surprising degree of motility and make some plants creatures to be avoided by things that can creep and fly.

The plant that traps insects is an extreme instance of the inventive range of evolution. Another is the strangler tree, described in Section 5. A vine that engulfs a tree and takes its place in the forest would seem to fulfill in the plant world the notion that natural selection is a contest between creatures "red in tooth and claw." In truth, such plants are rare. Co-operation is much more the rule, just as it is among animals. The reconquest of the blasted island of Krakatoa by plant life, the first time such a process had been observed by scientists, provided a beautiful demonstration of the interdependence of species. In an orderly succession, various kinds of plants, their seeds brought by wind, water and birds, prepared the way for one another until, at last, trees and grass were growing again in the vault of a fully re-established jungle. The community of plants in the desert has evolved a similarly co-operative adaptation to the shortage of water. The short-lived shallow-rooted annuals make room for one another by maturing smaller. Desert shrubs and bushes that must survive the year around have evolved another solution. By percolating chemicals into the soil that prevent the growth of other plants, including those of their own species, they stake out sufficient water-collecting territory for their own need. Now that this adaptation has been noted in the desert, it is being looked for in other climates, and it is thought to hold the explanation for the mixture and succession of plants in much more crowded provinces.

The last chapter in this section on evolution and ecology considers a wider community of life that comprises not only plants but animals. The color, configuration and odor of flowers are variously and wondrously designed to attract bees and other insects, birds and bats. In contrast, the reproductive organs of plants that depend upon the wind for pollination can scarcely be described as flowers at all.

An important new agent in the evolution of plants is man. The agricultural revolution dates back only 10,000 years. But already it is difficult to trace the ancestry of cultivated plants to the wild stock from which farmers bred them. Until the last half-century man was pretty much a blind agent of natural selection. Wheat and corn became unrecognizably different from their ancestral wild grasses as, by hit and miss, man learned to exploit the accidents of nature. Now that plant breeding is guided by scientific understanding of the genetic process, the evolution of domestic plants is proceeding under acceleration. New strains of wheat and corn are created at will today to meet specifications of soil and climate, to resist new pandemic infections and to multiply output per acre and per man hour.

These developments, in turn, are having considerable impact on man's social evolution. In the United States, agricultural output continues to ascend while the number of our farm families declines. Our corn-hog agriculture is being adopted in other countries, notably Western Europe and the U.S.S.R., and is yielding comparable immediate returns in the increase and improvement of nutrition. Hybrid corn may go down in history as the most revolutionary idea to issue from the New World since the Declaration of Independence.

THE EDITORS*

* Board of Editors: Gerard Piel (Publisher), Dennis Flanagan (Editor), Leon Svirsky (Managing Editor), James R. Newman, E. P. Rosenbaum, James Grunbaum (Art Director).

PART 1 GROWTH SUBSTANCES

I. THE AUXINS

by Victor Schocken

At high school in Yonkers, New York, Victor Schocken was inspired by his teachers in physics and chemistry to point his education toward a career in science. Graduating from New York University in 1942, he went on to take his master's at Oregon State College and his doctorate at the California Institute of Technology. There his work on plant physiology was interrupted by a stretch of wartime research on rocket propellants under the direction of Linus Pauling. His first appointment, as a research assistant in the photosynthesis laboratory at the University of Illinois, brought him into the thick of the famous "quantum yield" controversy surrounding the work of the great German scientist, Otto Warburg. He went with Warburg from Illinois to the National Institutes of Health in Bethesda, Maryland, and worked with him there until Warburg's return to Germany. Then, after a year as research fellow at Harvard and an appointment as biochemist at the Smithsonian Institution, Schocken came to the decision in 1952 to abandon research and go to medical school. He is now a resident in internal medicine at George Washington University Hospital in Washington, D. C.

II. THE CONTROL OF FLOWERING

by Aubrey W. Naylor

Born in Tennessee in 1915, Aubrey W. Naylor received all three of his degrees from the University of Chicago, where he held at various times the distinctions of Swift, University and Rockefeller fellowships. His talents and training as a plant physiologist were suppressed during the war years in favor of a temporarily acquired facility as a radio operator in the service of the United States Navy. He resumed his career in science as a National Research Council fellow at the Boyce Thompson Institute and went on to appointments at the University of Washington and Yale. In 1952, he was called to Duke University as associate professor of botany. His contribution to this book reflects his principal line of research, directed at elucidating the biochemical basis of plant physiology.

III. WHAT MAKES LEAVES FALL?

by William P. Jacobs

An associate professor of biology at Princeton University, William P. Jacobs graduated from Harvard College in 1942, then studied at the California Institute of Technology on a Sheldon traveling fellowship from Harvard, returned to Harvard as a junior fellow and took a Ph.D. in biology in 1946. He has been at Princeton since 1948. About the choice of his line of work he writes: "Under the influence of Professor Ralph H. Wetmore of Harvard and Professor Frits Went of California Institute of Technology, I decided to concentrate on trying to discover what internal factors *normally* control the growth and differentiation of plants. The control of leaf fall was picked as a 'warmup' problem, preparatory to applying similar quantitative methods to the more difficult problem of what is going on inside the plant in terms of cell differentiation."

IV. NEW GROWTH SUBSTANCES

by Frank B. Salisbury

Upon receiving his Ph.D. at the California Institute of Technology in 1956, Frank B. Salisbury went to Colorado Agricultural and Mechanical College (since renamed Colorado State University) as assistant professor of botany. He was born in Provo, Utah, and graduated from the University of Utah in 1951. At Cal Tech he studied plant physiology under James Bonner (page 128) and is now carrying forward his own investigation of the chemistry of flowering. Writing about science for the layman is an important extracurricular interest for Salisbury; while he was at Cal Tech, his entry in a science-writing contest sponsored by the faculty was awarded top honors by the editors of SCIENTIFIC AMERICAN.

THE AUXINS

by Victor Schocken

MOST people are aware of the far-reaching effects of hormones upon their bodily functions and even their personalities. It is less widely recognized that in plants as well as animals hormones regulate the chemical reactions that comprise the life processes of the organism. The hormones of plants, like those of animals, are chemical substances that are produced in one part of the organism and affect a physiological process in another part. In plants the hormones originate not in special glands but in buds or certain other growing points. Some of them have been isolated in pure form. Moreover, just as drugs have been synthesized to simulate activities characteristic of hormones of the human body, so too synthetic compounds similar to the plant hormones have recently been developed. In other words, the plants have not only their adrenalin but their Benzedrine (a synthetic analogue of adrenalin) as well.

Obviously this means that man now has a practical means for the practice of therapy and control of the plant kingdom on a large scale. These natural and synthetic chemicals, which have been given the general name "auxins," have a powerful effect on the growth and health of plants even when used in very tiny amounts. Some of them are already in wide use by farmers and gardeners as weed killers and in other, more subtle, capacities, but the full exploration of their possibilities has barely begun.

The first observations that clearly suggested the presence of a hormone in plants were made by Charles Darwin during his study of phototropism, or the tendency of plants to incline toward a

3

light source. This phenomenon had been observed long before Darwin, but he was the first to show that different parts of the plant were involved in receiving the stimulus and in responding to it. Working with the seedlings of canarygrass, oats, beans, and other grasslike plants, Darwin found that if the tip of the seedling was covered with a cap of tin foil or blackened glass, the plant failed to bend toward a light directed at it from one side. If, on the other hand, the seedling was buried in fine black sand and only the tip was exposed, the phototropic curvature did take place; in fact the whole plant bent through the sand toward the light when it was illuminated from only one side. Darwin also observed that if part of the tip was cut off, even as little as a tenth of an inch, the seedling no longer exhibited phototropism.

From these and many other experiments he concluded, as he reported in 1881 in *The Power of Movement in Plants,* that "when seedlings are freely exposed to a lateral light some influence is transmitted from the upper to the lower part, causing the latter to bend."

But how was the influence transmitted? The Danish botanist P. Boysen Jensen found that if a horizontal incision was made in the dark side of a unilaterally illuminated seedling, and a piece of mica was inserted in the slit, the stimulus was blocked and the seedling did not bend. The same operation on the illuminated side, however, did not interfere with the normal bending of the plant toward the light. Boysen Jensen concluded that the stimulus from the light passes down the dark side of the seedling.

He then cut off the upper part of a seedling, placed a drop of gelatin solution on the cut surface of the stump, and replaced the upper part, holding it in position by means of a ring of cocoa butter. When the replaced tip was then unilaterally illuminated, a decided curvature appeared in the part below the cut, which had been kept in the dark and was connected with the illuminated tip only through the gelatin. The stimulus had passed through the gelatin, a layer of nonliving matter. Clearly the transmission of the stimulus from the tip to the region of response did not depend on the vital process of the seedling.

It was A. Paál, working at the University of Utrecht in Holland, who finally showed that the phototropic response is due entirely to a growth substance which is asymmetrically distributed in the plant. He demonstrated that if the tip of a seedling was cut off and replaced so that it covered only one side of the stump, greater growth occurred on that side and marked curvature of the plant resulted. This experiment conclusively proved the movement of a growth-regulating substance from the tip of the seedling to the lower parts, and it showed in addition that if one side of the seedling receives a higher concentration of this substance, then that side grows more rapidly and the seedling bends in the opposite direction.

The problem now was to extract the unknown substance. Continuing the work at Utrecht, F. W. Went (see page 45) cut off the tips of several oat seedlings, placed them on a block of agar, and then placed the agar atop one side of a decapitated oat seedling. As in Paál's experiment, the seedling curved away from the block, showing that growth hormone from the tips had diffused through the agar into the plant (see diagram on page 7). Went found that the amount of curvature was proportional to the number of tips used, which served as a rough measure of the concentration of growth hormone in a block. This observation gave rise to the *Avena* test (named for the genus of plants that embraces oats), which is still a standard method of quantitatively assaying for growth substances. The present *Avena* test uses agar blocks, but a more precise standard of measurement than plant tips.

With a method of assay for growth-hormone activity at hand, biochemists became interested in this field of research. They could now determine the relative abundance of the hormone in various materials, and could follow the activity of the hormone through extractions, concentrations or other chemical treatment. If by means of the *Avena* test they could find some abundant, auxin-rich material, then a chemical isolation of the hormone would be possible. Fritz Kögl and his group at the University of Utrecht undertook that search. In the course of testing a great variety of substances, they found that human urine is rich in growth substance. They therefore obtained about 40 gallons of urine from a hospital and proceeded to concentrate the hormone activity by chemical treatments. They eventually obtained 40 milligrams of crystals that had an activity 50,000 times as great as that of the original urine. This tiny pile of material, no larger in aggregate bulk than a half-carat diamond, was so concentrated that, dissolved and diluted, it would have been sufficient to induce 10 degrees of curvature in each of two billion oat seedlings. Upon chemical analysis the active substance was found to be a new compound, $C_{18}H_{32}O_5$. It was named auxentriolic acid or auxin a.

In the same year, 1934, a second active substance was isolated from corn-germ oil by a similar procedure of extraction and concentration. This substance, which is quite similar to auxin a, has the formula $C_{18}H_{30}O_{40}$. It was called auxenolonic acid or auxin b. And finally, in the course of repeating the isolation from urine on a larger scale, the Kögl group isolated a third growth sub-

Oat-seedling experiment was performed by Frits W. Went to demonstrate the presence of auxin. In the first drawing the tip of the seedling A is cut off and placed on a block of gelatin. In the second drawing another oat seedling, B, is prepared as shown. In the third drawing the block of gelatin on which the tip of seedling A had rested is attached to the side of seedling B. In the last drawing seedling B has bent to the right, indicating that auxin which has been present in the tip of seedling A has stimulated the growth of cells on the left side of seedling B. The angle at which the seedling is bent is a measure of the amount of auxin.

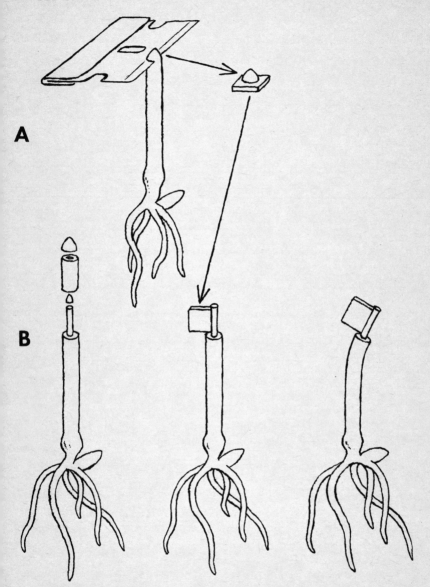

A

B

stance, indole-acetic acid, a compound which had been familiar to chemists for 50 years, though not until then recognized as a growth substance.

The problem remained to determine which of the three was the natural growth hormone in plants. By a process of elimination depending on the molecular weight and chemistry of the active material, it was determined to be auxin a, but more recently indole-acetic acid has also been isolated from plants. In any case, it was the discovery of the growth-promoting activity of the common chemical indole-acetic acid that made possible the vast research program that followed. Not only indole-acetic acid itself but many of its close chemical relatives, such as indole-propionic acid and naphthalene-acetic acid, were found to possess growth-promoting activity. Plant scientists were thus provided with an array of relatively simple and easily available organic compounds to use in further experimentation.

Indole-acetic acid has become the standard by which the growth-promoting activity of a substance is measured in the *Avena* test. The test is carried out in the following way: Seeds of a genetically pure strain of oats are stripped of their husks, are germinated on filter paper moistened with distilled water, and then are grown in glass holders. When the seedlings are about an inch high, the tips are removed, and the decapitated plants are divided into two groups. On one side of the stumps of one group are placed agar blocks containing known amounts of indole-acetic acid. On the other group are placed agar blocks of the same size and composition but containing the substance to be tested instead of indole-acetic acid. After 90 minutes of growth, all the seedlings are photographed and their curvatures are measured. By comparing the curvature produced by the unknown substance with that produced by indole-acetic acid, a quantitative estimate of the auxin activity of the unknown is obtained.

After their identification, the next important discovery about the auxins was that besides promoting the growth of seedlings they also influence the development of plant form and structure. It had long been known that while the main shoot of a plant is growing, its lateral buds are inhibited. If, however, the bud at the apex is cut off, the lateral buds begin to develop. It had been postulated that an inhibiting substance diffuses from the growing bud to the tissue below it. With the advent of synthetic growth substances this theory was corroborated. When the apical bud was removed from a shoot and a small quantity of indole-acetic acid was applied to the stump, the lateral buds did not develop. Thus indole-acetic acid, which in other experiments had been observed to promote growth, was found to possess the power to inhibit as well.

At about the same time it was demonstrated that the auxins have root-forming activity. This was another illustration of the versatile way in which auxins affect growing plants. But it also had an immediate practical importance, for experiments performed on a great variety of plants showed that auxin applications are generally beneficial in bringing about the rooting of cuttings. This process, known as vegetative propagation, is extremely useful to the horticulturist, for by means of it a great many genetically identical plants may be made from a single individual; and a desired genetic pattern, as in a variety of apple, a seedless orange, or a rose of a new color, may be preserved from generation to generation. In practice the cutting is usually a twig with a few leaves on it, but sometimes leaves, pieces of stem or root, or even bulb scales may be used to start a new plant. Auxin-treated cuttings generally root more rapidly than untreated ones, and the roots are more abundant and stronger. Dipping cuttings into auxin solutions or powders has become standard horticultural practice, and there are on the market today dozens of prepa-

9

rations designed for the nurseryman or home gardener. Incidentally, it has been discovered that this same ability to promote root growth is possessed by the petroleum product ethylene, which also has the property of accelerating the ripening of fruit. Ethylene is given off by certain varieties of quick-ripening apples, and if such apples are put in an airtight container with green tomatoes the tomatoes have been observed to ripen faster.

Another property of auxins that has grown to economic importance is their ability, when applied to the flowers of certain species, particularly the tomato, to initiate the development of fruit without pollination. Because of the difficulty of obtaining satisfactory pollination in a greenhouse where there are few insects and little wind, greenhouse growers of tomatoes are increasingly resorting to auxin treatments in the form of sprays or aerosol mists to improve fruit set. Fruits so induced are usually seedless; so besides increasing yields, auxin treatments may make possible the development of new seedless varieties.

In the raising of pineapples there is also some difficulty in obtaining satisfactory fertilization and development of the fruit. But here the problem is to obtain flowering of the plant at the proper time. The size to which the fruit develops is directly dependent on the number of leaves on the plant at the time of flowering. J. van Overbeek, working in Puerto Rico, found that the Cabezona variety of pineapple, which flowers poorly when left to itself, can be made to flower at any time of the year by a single application of an auxin (naphthalene-acetic acid or 2,4-dichlorophenoxyacetic acid). We therefore have the interesting possibility of producing uniform fruits of a selected size by applying the auxin to each plant when it has the appropriate number of leaves.

Although apples and pears need no such stimulation to flower and fruit abundantly, growers of these fruits use large amounts of auxins for still another purpose. One of the main sources of loss to apple and pear crops has been premature drop. From a fourth to half of the entire crop may be lost because the fruit falls before it has matured or developed good color. Thus the grower must either harvest before the best quality is attained or else risk a heavy fall. It had been observed that auxin applications delayed the fall of the leaves in *Coleus* plants, a genus of mint. Auxin sprays were therefore tried on apple trees to delay the fall of the fruit. This treatment proved highly successful, and now orchardists can obtain reasonable assurance against loss to their apple and pear crops by using any one of several specially prepared commercial auxin sprays.

Still another commercial application of auxins takes advantage of their growth-inhibiting ability. The methyl ester of naphthalene-acetic acid prevents the sprouting of potatoes in storage; thus the tubers will keep longer, even at warm temperatures. Nurserymen have found the same compound useful in storing quick-sprouting plants such as rosebushes.

One of the more recent additions to the auxin family is 2,4-D (2,4-dichlorophenoxyacetic acid). This compound has received wide acclaim as a weed-killer, for when sprayed on plants it kills the broad-leaved dicotyledons (the great subclass of seed plants that includes most herbs and shrubs), while sparing the grasses. Under favorable circumstances, therefore, it can be used to keep sugar-cane fields, cornfields, golf courses or lawns free from most common weeds without laborious hoeing or weeding. Recent experiments indicate that in the plants affected by 2,4-D there is a temporary sharp increase in the rate of metabolism. The sprayed plant is not only injured where the chemical comes in contact with it, but is stimulated to burn up its reserve food supply. As a consequence it starves to death. In smaller concentrations 2,4-D can also be used for most of the applications of auxins previously mentioned. It can even cure—by its lethal action in another area of the plant kingdom—the fungus infection athlete's foot. In fact, 2,4-D well illustrates the wide variety of responses that auxins can elicit from plants.

The great versatility of this hormone was graphically described in an account of a series of experiments by J. W. Mitchell in the *Yearbook of Agriculture* 1943–1947:

"For instance, if only a speck, about one millionth of an ounce, of 2,4-D is put on one side of the stem of a bean seedling, the cells along the treated side grow faster than those on the untreated side and the plant will bend sharply in a direction away from the treated surface. If, however, about 2,000 times that amount of 2,4-D (about as much of the powder as can be held on an eighth of an inch of the flat end of a toothpick) is mixed with a little lanolin and the mixture is rubbed on a tender section of the stem, the plant responds differently. Food materials within the plant are moved from other parts of the stem, and possibly from some of the leaves, into the treated section, where many new cells are formed. The new cells finally become organized and arranged so that they form new roots inside the stem. The young roots, called root primordia, later push their way to the outer surface of the stem, and if that part of the stem is covered with moist soil the primordia will grow out into it and function as ordinary roots do in supplying the plant with water and nutrients.

"If, on the other hand, the above-ground parts of the plant are sprayed or dusted with 2,4-D, the response is yet different, for leaf growth ceases, the rate of respiration of the plant is increased, and its reserve food materials are broken down and subsequently burned up. As a result the plant generally dies one to three weeks after treatment, or the length of time required for its reserve food materials to be depleted."

We can see now that while the activities of plant hormones parallel those in animals up to a point, the parallel is not complete. The auxins seem to be more general and versatile in their effects. Whereas an animal hormone is likely to control only a single process or reaction, an auxin may influence a plant in many different ways, at least so far as the physical effects are observable. Sometimes it stimulates growth; under other conditions it retards growth. Sometimes it induces a tumor. Sometimes it kills the entire plant. Such observations lead with increasing clarity to the conclusion that the auxins must influence some basic general cellular process, and that the result of this influence may be expressed in a variety of ways, depending on the nature and age of the tissue, on the availability of other interacting substances, and on the external and internal conditions.

Many investigators have concerned themselves with determining how the influence is effected and what reactions are involved; for to understand the mechanism regulating the growth and development of plants would indeed be a step toward understanding life itself. Theories have been proposed, of course, but they are little more than guides for further research, since none is supported by a sufficient body of facts and observations to be accepted as an explanation. Because the auxins affect the growth of plants in such small concentrations, it is widely believed that the auxins must play some role in an enzyme system, either directly, for example as coenzymes, or indirectly through chemical mediation. Although the identity of the enzyme involved in the response to auxins has not yet been established, it is to be hoped that work now in progress will eventually yield the long-sought explanation.

Meanwhile the chemical revolution in agriculture continues and the prospect of regulating the rate and pattern of plant growth by auxins gives promise of a new epoch of abundance through a hitherto unhoped-for control over nature.

THE CONTROL OF FLOWERING

by Aubrey W. Naylor

THE FIRST CROCUS blooms, heralding spring. As the year advances, other plants, each in its own season, will burst into flower on a predictable schedule. The calendar of blooms is so familiar that we take it for granted. But what is behind this predictability? Why not crocuses in July, or black-eyed Susans in April, or goldenrod in May?

Flowering represents a radical change in the physiology of a plant. Suddenly the plant turns from producing stems and leaves to making the blooms that will yield fruit and the seeds of reproduction. What master switch sets off this change? If we understood the mechanism that initiates plant flowering, we could envision some really breath-taking advances in agriculture and our control over nature.

Any study of the subject must begin with the environmental factors that govern a plant's development. Temperature, light, water and nutrition all play their parts, and clever gardeners and greenhousemen have long known how to force plants into bloom to meet deadlines by skillful manipulation of these influences. Their empirical methods have shed little light, however, on the physiological process that transforms a plant from the vegetative (foliage-producing) to the flowering state.

We know that a plant, like an animal, must reach a certain stage of maturity before it is ready to flower and reproduce. It takes fruit trees, for example, several years to begin bearing blossoms and fruit. A corn plant will not flower until it has produced a certain minimum number of leaves, the number depending on the variety of corn. There is a remarkable bamboo plant native to the mountains of Jamaica that carries the process of growing up to a strange extreme: 32 years after the plant is born, it flowers once and then dies. Its life cycle seems to be independent of the environment; transplanted to any other part of the world, the plant still blossoms on schedule at the age of 32 years, no earlier and no later.

What makes plants ripe to flower is not known. Occasionally a plant blooms ahead of schedule, just as an animal sometimes comes precociously to puberty. In animals precocious puberty can be induced by removing or impairing the pineal gland in the brain, which presumably changes the hormone balance of the body and accelerates sexual maturity. This suggests that hormones may have something to do with a plant's ripeness-to-flower.

Investigations to track down the physiological mechanism whereby a plant starts producing flowers have been carried out mainly along two lines, using two different tools to control flowering. The first is temperature. About 35 years ago the German plant physiologist Gustav Gassner discovered that he could influence the flowering of cereal plants by controlling the temperature of germinating seeds. One of the plants on which he experimented was winter rye. Winter rye is planted in the autumn, germinates during the winter and flowers the following summer. If it is planted in the spring, it fails to flower, remaining vegetative throughout the growing season. Gassner found, however, that by keeping the seed at near-freezing temperatures during germination he could make winter rye flower even when he planted it in late spring. This procedure was later adopted by plant breeders to transform winter cereals into spring types, and it became known as "vernalization."

At first it was thought that the low-temperature treatment changed a plant's general metabolism. But it developed that

15

vernalization was a reversible process; that the change took place during a critical four-day period, after which it could not be reversed, and that rye seedlings could not be vernalized if they were undernourished. All this indicates that flowering depends on the formation of certain specific substances in the plant, rather than on an alteration in its general metabolism.

The second tool used to investigate flowering is the response of plants to the length of day—what is known as photoperiodism. This tool has been far more fruitful than temperature; it has been utilized by a great many investigators in a great variety of experiments, and it has already yielded some important practical results in agriculture.

The fascinating story of photoperiodism goes back to a historic investigation more than 30 years ago by two workers in the U. S. Department of Agriculture—W. W. Garner and H. A. Allard. They wondered why the variety of tobacco called Maryland Mammoth was delayed in flowering when it was grown near Washington, D. C. It flowered so late in the season that its seeds did not mature. The two investigators tried growing the plant under various conditions and explored many blind alleys before they discovered the answer: at the critical time the days were too long and the nights too short for these plants at Washington. Maryland Mammoth tobacco is a short-day plant, meaning that it begins to form flowers when the days are between 10 and 12 hours long. In the Washington growing season the days do not become as short as this until late in the summer. Consequently the tobacco plant, though ripe to flower long before, is delayed in receiving the necessary stimulus and so flowers very late.

Garner and Allard went on to test and confirm this discovery with many other species of plants. They found that plants fell into three general categories: short-day, long-day and indeterminate (not choosy as to length of day). Photoperiodism at once accounted for many things which had long puzzled botanists. It provided a reasonable explanation of why plants of a given variety, even though planted at different times, will nevertheless all flower at the same time, and why certain plants flourish in some latitudes and are practically absent from others.

Ragweed, for instance, starts making flowers when the day is just about 14.5 hours long. At Washington this length of day occurs around July 1, and the plant flowers and sheds its pollen by the middle of August. It has ample time, in other words, to form and scatter its seeds before frost comes. But there is little or no ragweed in northern Maine. There the long summer days do not shorten to 14.5 hours until after August 1. Ragweed, starting to form flowers after that date, would generally be killed by frost before its seed matured. Hence even if the wind or birds should bring ragweed seed to northern Maine, the plant could not establish itself there.

Conversely, a plant that thrives in the North may fail to flower in more southern latitudes where the spring and summer days are shorter. For instance, the rock-garden plant *Sedum telephium,* which needs a day of 16 hours or more, blooms very well in southern Vermont but will not flower in Virginia. This is a common experience of gardeners; attracted by a colorful plant during a trip, they may take it home to transplant in the garden, only to find that while it grows splendidly, it never produces anything but shoots and leaves. For this disappointing and puzzling result, sensitivity to the length of day is apt to be responsible.

There is a variety of wild sugar cane which flowers only if the dark period is 10 to 12 hours long. Clearly, under natural conditions this species would be confined to the tropics. Spinach, on the other hand, would never flower or reproduce itself by seed in the tropics, because it must receive 14 hours of light per day for a period of at least two weeks. And so it goes for many other plants.

17

The discovery of photoperiodism's important role in limiting the range of plants was, of course, a matter of great consequence to agriculturalists. The United States Department of Agriculture now determines photoperiod requirements as a matter of routine before new plants are introduced. For instance, the various varieties of soybeans and onions are extremely sensitive to photoperiod; an individual variety may grow to its maximum only within a narrow belt of latitude as little as 150 miles wide and may fail as a crop if planted north or south of that region. Moreover, knowledge of photoperiod requirements is a great help to plant breeders. Sometimes they wish to cross two strains of plants that ordinarily flower in different months. By controlling the photoperiod in a greenhouse they can make the two strains flower at the same time and thereby fertilize each other. In this way breeders have obtained some valuable hybrid crop plants which could not be produced otherwise.

But photoperiodism has been most rewarding as a research tool. Very early the experimenters discovered a surprising fact. It seemed reasonable to suppose that if a plant required a certain length of day to flower, darkening the plant for part of the day should interfere with its flowering. This experiment was performed repeatedly, but nothing happened; the plants flowered just as if they had had a full day of light. Interruption of the nighttime period of darkness, however, told another story. Even a few minutes of illumination affected the plant's flowering. Thus when a short-day plant such as the chrysanthemum is illuminated for a few minutes in the middle of the night during the season when it normally would flower, it fails to bloom. On the other hand, a long-day plant such as pyrethrum can be made to flower in a short-day season when it would not normally do so, simply by exposing it to light for a short time at night. The critical factor in photoperiodism, then, is not the length of day but the length of night; strictly speaking, plants should be classified as long-night and short-night rather than short-day and long-day.

This information obviously has its practical uses. Flower growers, who used to delay chrysanthemum flowering for the late fall market by extending the daylight period with several hours of artificial light, now can achieve the same end and save a lot of current by illuminating the plants for a few minutes in the middle of the night.

More important, however, is the lead that this discovery has given in the investigation of the flowering process itself. Evidently the chemical reactions responsible for flowering go on in a plant at night. These reactions are sensitive to light. Other experiments show that they require carbon dioxide (or sugar sprayed on the leaves as a substitute) and depend on the quality (i.e., wave lengths) of the light—all of which indicates that the photoperiodic reactions are in some way linked with photosynthesis. However, they appear to depend on some pigment other than chlorophyll as the light receptor.

We come back, then, to the main question: What is the chemical basis of flowering? Nearly a hundred years ago the great German plant physiologist Julius von Sachs suggested that the leaves of a plant produce "flower-forming substances" which travel to the growing points where flowers are generated. The first laboratory evidence to support his theory was discovered in 1934 almost simultaneously by several different groups of workers —J. E. Knott at Cornell University, J. Kuijper and L. K. Wiersum in the Netherlands and M. C. Cajlachjan in the U.S.S.R. Knott experimented with spinach, a long-day plant. He exposed the leaves to long photoperiods and covered the stem growing-point for part of the day so it was on a short photoperiod. The plants flowered as readily as if the whole plant had been on long photoperiods. When he reversed the procedure, giving the growing points long photoperiods and the leaves short photoperiods, the effect was the same as if the whole plant had been on short photoperiods—that is, the plant failed to flower. These experiments, confirmed and extended to other plants by the other workers, made it clear that the stimulus for flower formation must originate in the leaves. This strongly supported the idea that the stimulus was some kind of chemical regulator that moved from the leaves to the stem growing-points where flowers are formed.

Karl Hamner and James Bonner at the University of Chicago soon found even more convincing evidence. They did their work with cocklebur, a common noxious weed. This short-day plant is an ideal experimental tool for studying photoperiodism: it is sensitive to differences of less than 30 minutes in the dark period, a single nine-hour dose of darkness can induce it to flower, and it will survive considerable mutilation. Hamner and Bonner first stripped all the full-grown leaves from the plant and exposed the defoliated stem to nine-hour periods of darkness to see whether the plant would flower. It did not. But they found that when they left as little as one eighth of a fully expanded leaf on the stem, the plant did flower after exposure to the proper dose of darkness (see drawings opposite). By further experiments—forcing the plant to produce two branches, grafting shoots with leaves on the stem, and so on—they went on to show that the flower-induc-

Cockleburs flower upon exposure to flower-inducing light cycle *(rectangles)* when only one eighth of a leaf remains on a plant *(third from left at top)* and when only one leaf is exposed to the light. Leafless plants and those exposed to other light cycles did not flower. This indication that a chemical originating in the leaves caused the plants to flower was supported by the experiments with branched and grafted plants shown in the two lower panels. Even the placing of a piece of paper across the graft *(bottom right)* did not keep the unlighted plant from flowering when the other was exposed to the flower-inducing cycle.

20

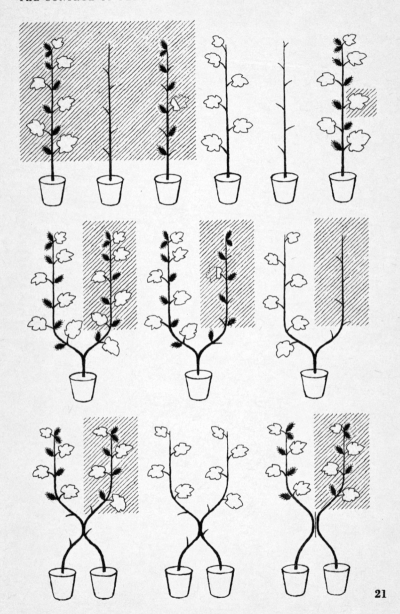

ing stimulus can travel up and down in the stem and across graft unions. They were also able to make a rough estimate of the rate of movement of the stimulus.

Many other investigators now took up the scent. Experimenting with a wide variety of plants, they demonstrated the activity of the flower-inducing stimulus in some striking ways. A nonflowering plant can be made to flower by grafting on to it a single leaf from a flowering plant, or even an isolated leaf that has been exposed to the proper amount of light. The stimulus can travel a considerable distance through several grafts. In one stunt six double-branched cocklebur plants were grafted together in series and all the leaves were removed except one at the tip of the last plant. After this leaf was exposed to dark periods of the appropriate length, the whole series of grafted plants proceeded to flower in orderly sequence down the chain!

The flower-promoting stimulus is not special and different in each species of plant; apparently it is some general factor common to all plants. This is shown by the fact that a plant can be induced to bloom by a leaf graft from another variety, species, genus or even from another family of plants. There is a certain parasitic plant, growing underground on the roots of red clover, that apparently obtains the flower-inducing factor from its host!

How can the same factor cause flowering both in long-day and short-day plants, which respond so differently to light? One working hypothesis is that the factor is a substance which promotes flowering when it reaches a certain minimum concentration and inhibits flowering when it accumulates to a higher concentration. According to this theory, suggested by Harry Borthwick and Marion Parker of the Beltsville Experiment Station, a plant that is ripe to flower produces the active substance continuously, but the substance is unstable to light. In a long-day plant, the substance is somehow protected from destruction by light so that it does not fall below the minimum concentration needed for flowering; such a plant will flower even if exposed to light continuously. In darkness, however, the substance accumulates in the plant, and if the night is too long, it accumulates to the point where it inhibits flowering. When the plant is illuminated in the middle of the night, the light destroys the excess substance and enables the plant to flower. In a short-day plant, on the other hand, the flower-promoting substance is not protected from the destructive effects of daylight. Hence the plant needs a long period of uninterrupted darkness to accumulate enough of the substance to flower.

All in all the evidence seems overwhelmingly in favor of the idea that a flower-promoting hormone does exist. The Russian worker Cajlachjan succumbed to the temptation to name the suspected substance "florigen." The potential value of this powerful substance, if indeed it exists, is so obvious that many attempts have been made to extract and isolate it from plants, in the United States and abroad. So far none has succeeded, though hopes have been raised several times. One of the difficulties is that no one knows just how such a substance should be introduced into a plant to promote flowering; hence experimenters cannot be certain whether they have failed to find the correct substance or simply failed to apply it properly.

Some investigators believe that plant hormones already known, rather than special "florigens," may be the agents responsible for the control of flowering. They argue that the growth-promoting hormones known as auxins may regulate flowering as well as vegetative growth.

One of the auxins is indole-acetic acid. It has been found that when the cocklebur plant is grown on long photoperiods, unfavorable for flowering, it produces much more indole-acetic acid than when it is on short photoperiods. This would indicate

23

that the auxin inhibits flowering. There are some obvious ways to test that conclusion: anything that neutralizes or destroys auxin in the plant should promote flowering, and an artificial increase in the plant's supply of auxin should suppress flowering. Experiments indicate that this is indeed the case. When cocklebur plants are treated with X rays or certain chemicals that are known to destroy or counteract auxin, the plants flower more profusely than they would normally. On the other hand, treatment with auxins interferes with flowering. James Bonner and John Thurlow at the California Institute of Technology have prevented flowering in the cocklebur by treating the plant with indole-acetic acid, and the writer has greatly delayed flowering in plants by treating them with other auxins.

There is now good evidence that plants themselves produce natural substances which counteract auxins. These indirect indications point to the conclusion that flowering is regulated by the balance between the auxins and their antagonists in the plant.

We are still far short of solving the mystery of what makes plants flower. It will take a great deal of investigation to determine just what substances are involved, how they are formed in the plant, and how they interact. Nevertheless, the information so far obtained has already made it possible to control flowering by chemical methods in a few plants.

One of these is the pineapple. This crop used to be expensive to produce, because the plants flowered and set fruit erratically, so that pickers had to come back to a field again and again to collect fruit as it ripened. Now all this has changed, thanks to the discovery that various substances, notably acetylene and naphthalene-acetic acid, can control the flowering of pineapple. Six to eight weeks after treatment a whole field flowers with amazing uniformity. As a result pineapple crops can now be harvested with all the techniques and machinery of mass production. The plants are usually treated with naphthalene-acetic acid, but this treatment has a drawback: the fruit-bearing stalks grow too weak and topple over. This can be corrected, however, by spraying the plants at the proper time with B-naphthoxyacetic acid. One of the leading investigators in the field, J. van Overbeek, observes wryly that the pineapple growers still are not satisfied: they want treatments that will make the fruits grow tailor-made to fit the cans!

Chemical control promises to make another dream come true. Hawaiian growers have long wished they could achieve large-scale production of the litchi nut, one of the most delicious of all tropical tree fruits. The litchi tree has been a poor performer in Hawaii; only about four per cent of the trees flower and bear fruit. Now it seems that naphthalene-acetic acid may be the answer. In recent experiments it has been found that when litchi trees are sprayed with this growth substance at the end of September, about 88 per cent of the trees bear fruit. Development of this discovery may create a new industry in the Hawaiian Islands.

Some work has also been done with vegetable and grain crops. Among the promising candidates for control are lettuce and celery. The problem here is to prevent flowering, because lettuce and celery are grown for their vegetative parts (leaves and stalks) and lose their market value when they begin to go to seed. In the case of lettuce, experimenters have succeeded in delaying the development of seed stalks and flowers by treating the seeds of the plant with cold and a chemical at the time when they are germinating. In the case of celery, they have found one chemical treatment that retards flowering and another that accelerates it. Celery growers who grow celery for the table can use one, and those who grow it for seed can use the other. Tobacco is another plant in which it is desirable to prevent flowering, and some promising results have been obtained with that crop.

But of all plants, perhaps the most important candidate for research on the control of flowering is corn, the number one United States crop. Such research has already started, with two ends in view. One is to regulate flowering so that desirable strains which do not ordinarily flower at the same time can be crossed. The other is to sterilize corn tassels by chemical means. Growers of hybrid seed corn must sterilize the tassels to prevent plants from fertilizing themselves and reproducing their own kind; to produce the hybrid seed it is necessary to fertilize the plants with pollen from selected strains. At present the plants are generally de-tasseled by hand—an expensive operation. Chemical sterilization obviously would be much easier and less costly.

For both of the control purposes, promising experimental leads have already developed. Spraying with 2,4-D, the well-known weed killer, delays flowering in corn without harming the ear. And the tassel can be sterilized by treatment with the plant-growth inhibitor maleic hydrazide.

The results so far in the chemical control of flowering have been highly promising, in some cases even spectacular, and the future is bright. When the flowering process is fully understood, progress will, of course, be much faster. We may even be able to force into bloom plants that now flower rarely.

WHAT MAKES LEAVES FALL?

by *William P. Jacobs*

THE FALLING of the sere and yellow leaf symbolizes autumn, but leaf fall is not limited to that season. All summer long in temperate zones and all the year round in the tropics there is a steady, though inconspicuous, rain of leaves from trees. Plants continually shed tissues (not only leaves but also fruits, flowers and other organs) as the organs grow old. This gives them certain enviable advantages denied to most of the animal kingdom. If man, for example, could shed his aging extremities and grow new ones to take their place, Renoir would not have had to strap his brush to his old and trembling hand in order to paint what his still "young" mind could conceive.

Botanists have been trying for nearly a century to discover the process by which plants shed their leaves. One of the first clues that attracted their attention was the fact that some plants develop a distinct layer of cells at the base of the leaf stalk and the leaves then break off at that point. But the so-called "separation layer" proved to be a false clue. Many plants have no such layer, and many others have one but their leaves do not separate at that place.

The leaf-shedding process, whatever its physiology, is speeded in the autumn by the shortening of the day; this was confirmed long ago by experiments which demonstrated that when the day was lengthened by artificial light, trees held their leaves later than usual. But various other factors also were found to influence the process. And among these the one that has been the greatest help in unraveling the mystery is the observation, made almost

100 years ago, that when the blade of a leaf is cut off or severely damaged, the leaf stalk falls off the plant very soon afterward.

This lead has been pursued with much zest and profit in recent years by laboratory experiments. For precise and extensive experimentation trees are remarkably inconvenient. Most of us do not have a musculature which would make us look forward to manipulating oaks and maples. And trees take so long to do almost anything! So for the same reasons that animal biologists are much better acquainted with the physiology of mice than of elephants, plant physiologists like to work with greenhouse plants. The favorite plant for studying leaf fall is the familiar house plant *Coleus,* also called the "beefsteak plant" because of its deep red leaves. When grown in the greenhouse under the cultural conditions which we have used for our experiments, Coleus keeps a fairly constant number of leaves on its main stem. Every seven to ten days the oldest pair of leaves falls off at the bottom of the stem and a new pair forms at the apex. Coleus has the further great advantage that it is easy to grow from cuttings, so that a large collection of genetically identical plants can be developed from a single original parent. In our experiments we have used some 3,000 plants, all derived from one original plant: in effect our subjects have been "identical twins" multiplied 1,500 times! With this uniformity of heredity, it is possible to measure reliably very small treatment effects even with small sample sizes.

The two major parts of a leaf are the flat blade and the stalk by which the blade is attached to the plant stem. As we just noted, when the blade of a leaf is cut off, the remaining leaf stalk soon separates and drops from the stem. For instance, a young, fast-growing Coleus leaf, which normally takes 35 to 40 days to reach the age of natural fall, will fall in only five or six days if it is debladed. The first substantial hint as to the internal mechanism controlling fall came when it was found that even if only a tiny piece of the leaf blade was left on the stalk, the leaf would stay on the stem just as long as if it had a complete blade. This indicated that the substance in the blade that prevented the fall of the leaf must be active in very minute amounts. It could not be a general nutrient such as sugar; most likely it was a hormone.

The hormone was soon identified. It is the plant growth substance, auxin. An alert German investigator applied the hormone to debladed Coleus leaves and found that the substance not only kept the leaves growing but "increased their longevity," that is, delayed their fall.

It was later established that the leaf blades of Coleus produce substantial amounts of auxin, and a clear and direct relation between auxin production and leaf fall was worked out. The more auxin a leaf produces, the longer it takes to fall. The fastest-growing leaves produce most auxin; the maximum production occurs when the young leaf is 60 to 100 millimeters long (between two and a half and four inches). The oldest leaves produce little or no auxin.

Quantitative experiments, in which synthetic auxin was applied to debladed leaves in the amounts that would normally be manufactured by the blade, showed that it had exactly the same effect in inhibiting leaf fall. The general conclusion was that auxin produced in the leaf blade moves down into the leaf stalk, and there inhibits leaf fall in direct relation to how much auxin there is. This conclusion was confirmed in a qualitative way for the leaves of other plants and for a number of kinds of fruits. In fact, spraying apple trees with auxin has become a fairly routine method of preventing premature dropping of the fruit.

The control of leaf fall by auxin seemed to be completely clear. It was, in fact, *too* clear. As often happens when our interpretations of nature seem marvelously simple, the simplicity turns out to reside in us, not in nature.

While thinking over this theory of leaf fall, I was struck by the odd circumstance that each leaf seemed to be acting as an independent entity. The theory implied that the fall of a leaf depended only on how much auxin was coming into its stalk from its own blade. Now in most cases that we know of, the behavior or development of one part of a plant is subject to inhibitions and stimulations from other parts of the plant. One therefore had to suspect the completeness of the hypothesis that leaf fall was totally independent of influence from the rest of the plant. Furthermore, while the hypothesis seemed to explain what prevented leaves from falling, it left unclear what causes them to fall when they do.

With these thoughts in mind, we planned some experiments to try to detect influences from the rest of the plant. These involved trials of various patterns in deblading the leaves of a plant. Coleus leaves grow in pairs, the two members of each pair coming from opposite sides of the stem. The usual practice had been to deblade one of each pair, leaving the "sister" leaf intact as a control. Now, if the fall of each leaf was controlled independently within itself, it should be immaterial in what pattern the leaves up the stem were debladed, or how many of them were. But experiments showed that the pattern of deblading did make a consistent, though small, difference in the time of leaf fall, and that when *all* the leaves (except those in the bud at the apex of the stem) were debladed, the fall was strikingly slowed down!

The most obvious conclusion was that the presence of intact leaves in some way speeded the fall of debladed leaves. Indeed, their presence accelerated the fall even of old leaves that were not debladed, for when the blades were removed from all the younger leaves, the old ones remained on longer than they would have otherwise.

It seemed, then, that leaf blades produce not only a substance (auxin) which inhibits falling but also a substance which speeds falling. What might this substance be? The most likely candidate was ethylene. This ingredient of illuminating gas has long been known to cause trees' leaves to fall, and recently it has been learned that some ethylene is naturally present in plant tissues; it is emitted by ripening fruit and by leaves. However, we were unable in an extensive series of experiments to find any evidence that ethylene from leaves speeded leaf fall.

Although we scoured the research literature, we could find no other leads that proved fruitful. We therefore decided to look more closely at the experimental plants. It was then we noticed something we should have seen before. In every experiment we had left untouched the tiny leaves in the apical bud at the top of the stem. And every treatment that speeded the fall of leaves lower on the stem had at the same time accelerated the growth of the apical leaves. We now noticed a clear correlation between this growth and the time of the debladed leaves' fall. They fell just when the bottom leaves of the apical bud above them reached a length of 70 to 80 millimeters. Fast leaf fall seemed to be closely tied up with the presence just above of leaves 70 to 80 millimeters long.

Why should this particular length of the apical leaves be so important? The answer is that when a leaf reaches this size it attains its maximum production of auxin. It was beginning to look as if the primary cause of speeded leaf fall was auxin production by the apical bud leaves above the debladed leaves. Further analysis indicated that the presence of intact leaves lower on the stem speeds leaf fall indirectly by speeding the growth of these apical leaves.

This view was confirmed by the following experiment. Many plants were prepared in which the young leaves were debladed and the older leaf pairs left intact. As in earlier experiments, the presence of the older leaves low on the stem speeded the fall of the debladed leaves above them, so long as the apical bud was left intact. But when the apical bud was cut off, the debladed leaves in that set of plants fell much more slowly. If, however, synthetic auxin was applied in place of the cut-off bud, the debladed leaves fell as fast as if the bud were on. Thus the experiments confirmed our surmise that auxin from the apical bud speeds the fall of debladed leaves.

These experiments, along with others which there is not space to describe, show that the fall of leaves is controlled by an "auxin-auxin balance." Auxin both slows and speeds leaf fall. So long as a leaf's own blade produces enough auxin to overcome the effect of auxin coming from younger leaves above, the leaf will stay on the plant. But as soon as its production of auxin drops to less than the critical rate—because of old age, too much shade, insect attack or deblading—the auxin from the younger, more vigorous leaves above causes the leaf to fall. Such a system has obvious adaptive value. The old and infirm are shed by the action of a hormone from the young and vigorous.

It is a great surprise that the same hormone should act as both the stimulator and the inhibitor of leaf fall. Apparently its contrary effects depend simply on the direction from which it comes. We can only marvel at the frugality of nature, which has endowed plants with a single hormone that can do so many different things.

So much for Coleus. How much of this applies to trees? Since detailed experiments of the sort described here have never been done with trees, we do not know. In fact, it seems unlikely that such experiments ever will be done on trees: to perform tree experiments equivalent to those with our 3,000 genetically identical Coleus plants one would need some 10,000 trees grown from seed. However, there is reason to believe that an auxin-auxin balance is at work in trees as in Coleus. Artificial lengthening of the daylight has been found to increase the amount of auxin produced by the blades of tree leaves. The fast growth of a new branch in spring is accompanied by the production of a big gush of auxin by the new branch, which presumably speeds the fall of the older leaves.

There is as yet no evidence as to the role of auxin in the shedding of leaves by trees in the autumn. But until more specific evidence is available, we will adopt the biologist's usual attitude in such cases: "Organisms are presumed the same until proved different." According to such a view the leaves of a tree, like the leaves of Coleus, remain on the tree until their own production of auxin becomes so small that auxin produced by other leaves can force them to fall.

NEW GROWTH SUBSTANCES

by Frank B. Salisbury

In the year 1926 a young Dutch botany student in Utrecht performed a simple but historic little experiment with oat seedlings. By day Frits Went was serving in the Dutch Army, working in the gas warfare division, but at night he would repair to his father's plant-physiology laboratory at the university to keep up his graduate studies in botany. Went and his fellow students were intensely interested in certain experimental investigations of the growth of plants that had been started by several European botanists, and they spent many a midnight hour arguing about the meaning of these curious experiments. Various tests of the effects of removing and replacing the tip of an oat seedling had indicated that the tip produced some substance which controlled growth of the sheath (coleoptile) covering the stem.

Went thought of a test which might settle the issue as to whether there really was such a substance. He cut off the tip of an oat seedling, laid it on a small block of gelatin and let the tip stand on the gelatin for several hours. Then he discarded the tip and attached the block of gelatin alone to the side of a decapitated seedling. If the hypothetical growth substance had diffused from the tip into the gelatin, his experiment should show an effect on the growth of the decapitated stem. And so it turned out. The side of the stem to which the gelatin was attached grew faster than the other side, so that the stem bent (see drawing on page 7).

It was 3 A.M. on the morning of April 17, 1926, that Went saw the successful result of his experiment. That moment is a milestone in the history of the study of how living things grow. Went's ingenious demonstration led to the isolation and identification of the plant growth hormones now known as auxins—substances which play a key role in the growth of roots, stems and buds; the development of fruit, and the falling of fruits and leaves. The auxins have become an immensely useful tool in plant culture, serving many purposes from the propagation of cuttings to the killing of weeds. Besides this, Went's experiments laid the foundation for most of what is now known about the mechanism of plant growth.

In 1956, just 30 years after Went's discovery of auxin, there came another milestone of a similar kind. On the afternoon of August 28, 1956, plant scientists assembled at Storrs, Connecticut, to hear the first collective report on exciting new developments in the investigation of plant growth. The subject of this conference, sponsored by the American Institute of Biological Sciences, was "Growth Regulators Other than Auxins." The new field opened up by the work reported at that meeting may well turn out to be even more important than the studies that grew from Went's discovery. Certainly the "growth regulators other than auxins" are going to touch the lives of all of us—not only in the classroom but on the farm and at the dinner table as well.

To show why I believe this to be true, I am going to review briefly some of the highlights of the talks given that day. Five men summarized work which is going on in many laboratories in the United States, England, Japan and elsewhere.

F. C. Steward of Cornell University told about a group of substances which have become known as the "coconut milk factors." In most species of plants the new seedling starts its growth on food stored in the seed. In the coconut this food is contained in the milk. When a coconut germinates, the embryonic seed leaf (cotyledon) within the shell feeds on the milk and grows rapidly by cell division until it fills the cavity of the nut. In 1941 J. van

Overbeek, while working at the Cold Spring Harbor Laboratory on Long Island, discovered that coconut milk could also stimulate the growth of embryos of the Jimson weed, a member of the potato family. Steward's group at Cornell has followed up this finding and sought to identify the growth-promoting substances in coconut milk.

They found that when the milk is added to a test-tube culture of carrot tissue, it produces a remarkable speed-up of the growth and division of the carrot cells. This technique therefore provides a means of testing the activity of the various ingredients of coconut milk. Identification of the active components has been an arduous and time-consuming task. From about 660 gallons of coconut milk the Cornell workers extracted about 26 pounds of a dark, heavy syrup which they then fractionated into a number of substances, many of which were identified as amino acids or other nutrients. They have so far isolated four substances which show growth-stimulating activity. One of these has been definitely identified as diphenylurea—though urea is usually thought of as an animal product. It is the first compound of this type that has been found in a plant extract. Synthetic analogues of this compound are known, however, to be powerful weed killers—which may be more than a coincidence.

The Cornell group finds that the growth-stimulating factors in coconut milk interact in significant ways with other substances. For instance, the activity of some of them is greatly enhanced when amino acids from the milk protein casein are added to the culture. On the other hand, coconut milk is counteracted by certain other materials, including extracts from the potato tuber. Yet potato tissue itself can be made to grow on a simple culture medium if coconut milk and a small amount of the weed-killing auxin 2,4-D are added!

Steward pointed out that all this suggests the normal growth of a plant is a balance between stimulators (e.g., the coconut milk factors) and inhibitors (e.g., the inhibiting substances in potato tubers). As the plant matures, the inhibitors may accumulate so that cell division slows down and finally stops. The unrestrained growth of tumors in plants (and possibly in animals?) may be the result of a disturbance of the balance between stimulators and inhibitors.

By means of the test-tube carrot culture the Cornell group has discovered growth promoters in other plants besides the coconut. They have extracted stimulating material from immature bananas, ginkgo fruit, walnuts, horse chestnuts, corn (in the milky stage) and from certain plant tumors. A stimulator in immature horse chestnuts has been identified as a colorless relative of the pigments in flower petals.

After Steward's report, R. H. Goodwin of Connecticut College reviewed the work of various laboratories on another group of plant substances known as unsaturated lactones. In contrast to the coconut factors, the lactones have long been recognized as plant substances and are well known chemically. But their significance to plant growth is just beginning to be understood.

In general, they seem to be inhibitors. The effects upon root growth are especially interesting. Goodwin and his students have shown that the concentration of certain lactones and their derivatives in some plant roots increases as the growth of the root cells decreases. A number of workers have been interested in just how the unsaturated lactones inhibit cell growth. Among other things, these lactones are known to interfere with certain enzyme systems. Since the systems in question are of a common type, the unsaturated lactones may turn out to be important in a number of phases of the growth process. This seems especially likely because they are so widely distributed in plants. One can't help but think of Steward's suggestion that growth is a balance between coconut factors and unknown inhibitors. Will those inhibitors turn out to be unsaturated lactones?

37

The lactones may also be highly important in plant ecology. Some of them (e.g., coumarin, found in the tonka bean and certain other plants) are known to inhibit the germination of seeds, and anything that prevents seeds from sprouting must have a powerful influence on the make-up of a plant community. Went, who has been at the California Institute of Technology since 1933, has found that desert plants carry on a continual chemical warfare by means of inhibitors against rivals. This phenomenon is discussed in the chapter "The Ecology of Desert Plants," by Went, beginning on page 146, and by James Bonner in his chapter, "Chemical Sociology Among the Plants," beginning on page 156. Bonner and some of his students at Cal Tech have isolated and identified compounds produced by some desert plants which are toxic to other plants. Three of these are unsaturated lactones. Thus a study of these substances might open up whole new vistas of understanding to the plant ecologist.

Kenneth V. Thimann of Harvard University, the chairman of the conference, next reported on work on another group of substances in which the leaders have been Folke Skoog, Carlos O. Miller and F. M. Strong of the University of Wisconsin, who were unable to attend the symposium. The principal substance in this group is a compound called kinetin, which is a derivative of adenine, one of the building blocks of the nucleic acids, the vitally important components of all cells. The Wisconsin group has found that kinetin will stimulate cells of the tobacco plant to divide in a culture in which they would not do so otherwise.

Kinetin has been extracted from the sperm of the herring and from other organisms. A substance with similar activity has been found in yeast extract and other plant products. Various other adenine derivatives active in causing cell division have been synthesized.

Kinetin or its relatives will cause a tobacco stem grown on a culture medium to form a greatly increased number of buds.

There is an interplay between auxin and kinetin: the more auxin in the culture medium, the more roots are formed; the more kinetin, the more buds. Kinetin and its relatives will promote expansion of leaf disks and germination of lettuce seed. Further, kinetin and auxin will imitate exactly the effects of certain bacteria in producing plant tumors.

Very likely many problems of both normal and abnormal plant growth will be illuminated by future work with kinetin. Among other things, it may tell a great deal about why plants take the shapes they do.

Probably the report that many of us at the symposium looked forward to most eagerly was the one on the gibberellins. F. H. Stodola, a chemist at the Northern Regional Research Laboratory in Illinois, reviewed the history of the gibberellin research and told about recent work on their chemistry.

It is a striking commentary on the poverty of international communication that the Western world has only just begun to pay attention to these important substances, although they were discovered in Japan as early as 1926—even before Went's discovery of the auxins! The Japanese knew that a fungus, *Gibberella fujikuroi,* caused a disease of rice, called "foolish seedling" disease because it made young rice plants grow ridiculously tall. A plant pathologist found that extracts of the fungus could produce the disease, and, after 12 years of concerted effort, workers at the University of Tokyo isolated an active substance which they named gibberellin A. By the time of Pearl Harbor the Japanese had published seven papers on the substance, and six of these had been abstracted in the United States. Twelve more Japanese papers appeared during the war. Yet it was not until 1950 that anyone outside Japan began to study gibberellin. Among the first were Stodola and his group in Illinois and P. W. Brian and his associates at the Imperial Chemical Industries in England. Since 1955 United States interest in the gibberellins has risen to a feverish high.

At least three gibberellins have now been isolated from the culture liquor of the fungus. All of these are acids with a complex structure. It is interesting to note that part of the structure is that of a lactone, which makes the gibberellins technically members of the lactone group.

Plant physiologists have been eagerly investigating the growth-regulating properties of these compounds. B. O. Phinney of the University of California at Los Angeles was chosen to tell the symposium about some of this work. The gibberellins have been applied to a large number of plants, and have produced quite a variety of responses. The most consistent and striking response is a marked elongation of the plant's stems. In citrus trees gibberellin causes the stems to lengthen more than sixfold! In a survey of 42 plant species, including grasses, trees, beets, beans, peanuts and so on, only three—the white pine, the onion and the gladiolus —failed to respond by stem elongation.

The gibberellins have a very interesting effect upon some dwarf plants. Brian has found that they cause a dwarf ("bush") pea to grow as tall as a "pole" pea plant, and Phinney has made five out of nine dwarf mutants of corn grow to normal height by treatment with gibberellin. Eleven other growth stimulators, including auxin, failed in this test. Is it possible that normal corn or peas produce gibberellin or gibberellinlike substances? There is now reason to believe that they may, for the U.C.L.A. workers have discovered that the five dwarf mutants of corn can be stimulated to grow to normal height by extracts taken from young seeds of a number of different plants.

The gibberellins also promote flowering of some plants. Some of these plants normally flower in response to the cold of winter; others respond to the lengthening of the day in spring, and some require a combination of both temperature and length of day.

So far about a dozen such species have been brought into flower out of season by exposure to gibberellins. Strangely, plants which require the short days of autumn to flower do not seem to respond to gibberellins in this way. Where applicable, however, this effect of the gibberellins may prove to be of great commercial value to seed growers.

So it appears that great things await plant physiologists as they begin to examine the substances discussed above. The auxins alone have kept students of plant growth busy for 30 years. Now there are four new groups of growth substances to explore—though it seems possible that the four may merge into a smaller number, for the coconut factors resemble kinetin in action, and the gibberellins appear related to the unsaturated lactones in chemistry.

It seems significant that within each group of compounds the individual members display considerable variation in behavior. These variations may be important. Physiologists have hitherto emphasized the similarities in basic processes (e.g., respiration) among all living organisms, but it is time to ask the question: How do species of plants and animals *differ* in their physiological functions? Concrete, meaningful answers may be forthcoming from studies of the plant-growth regulators. The stimulating factors obtained from horse chestnuts seem to be clearly different from those obtained from coconuts. How many of the higher plants have gibberellinlike substances? In what amounts and to what ends? These are new and exciting questions.

All the textbook notions of plant growth will have to be reexamined in the light of the new research. Some of them will stand and some will fall. Fascinating new problems beckon. Will this new understanding of normal growth help us to solve the problem of cancer?

PART 2 AGROCLIMATOLOGY

CLIMATE AND AGRICULTURE
by Frits W. Went

The mentor of a half dozen other contributors to this volume, Frits W. Went is professor of plant physiology at the California Institute of Technology. He was born in the Netherlands, the son of a professor of botany at the University of Utrecht. It was not his father, who was concerned not to push the boy into his field, but his high-school teacher who made Went a biologist—"he had no inhibitions in acquainting me with the endless problems of nature." For his Ph.D. in 1927, Went investigated the plant growth hormone, auxin; this classic work is described by one of his pupils on page 3. The present article bespeaks his second major scientific interest, the ecology of plants. To further his investigations in this field, Went designed and built at Cal Tech the world's most extraordinary greenhouse, the "phytotron," which is the principal protagonist in this chapter. The past decade's work in this laboratory has laid the foundation for the new science of "agroclimatology."

CLIMATE AND AGRICULTURE

by Frits W. Went

I N OUR elaborately industrialized country we tend to lose sight of the fact that modern man's life still depends fundamentally on agriculture. And it is difficult to appreciate how insecure this foundation is, from the standpoint of feeding a growing population. Only by prodigies of toil and invention has civilized man been able to wrest enough food from the soil to keep pace with his increasing needs. The invention of systematic agriculture was itself a remarkable technical achievement: to make it possible the original farmers had to develop crop plants (wheat, rice and so forth) and techniques of plowing, sowing, irrigation, weeding and fighting pests and diseases. Nowadays farming is a highly sophisticated technology. By mass-production methods each farm worker now can produce enough food for 17 persons; research has brought most of the important crop diseases and pests under effective control; scientific soil management makes it possible to get high yields from the same soil year after year; transportation facilities mitigate local crop failures by distributing food quickly over whole continents; modern preserving methods make fresh food available all year round.

The one great factor that man has not yet learned to control is climate. Droughts, floods, freezes, tornadoes, hailstorms still make farming an uncertain enterprise, even in the United States. And more subtle climatic aberrations may work even more havoc upon our crops.

The latter point is brought into sharp focus by a look at the annual figures for production of tomatoes in the United States.

The yield of tomatoes per acre in many states fluctuates enormously from one year to another. It is less variable in California than in states with more changeable climates. There cannot be much doubt that differences in weather from year to year are mainly responsible for these variations in yield. A number of other crops, such as beans, peas and various fruits, also suffer from climatic vicissitudes. What are these damaging climatic influences, so unobtrusive that it is difficult to detect them, let alone measure their effects? Plainly they must have to do with factors such as the amount of sunlight, temperature and humidity.

For nearly a decade we have been carrying on an investigation of the effects of climatic factors on plant production in our "phytotron" at the California Institute of Technology. It all began with a study of the growth of tomato plants under controlled conditions. The generosity of Miss L. Clark and the technical and scientific knowledge of H. O. Eversole had provided two fully air-conditioned greenhouses, and I decided to study first the response of plants to the relative humidity of the air. Since the temperature had to be high to produce a low enough humidity, I chose the tomato, a warmth-loving plant, as the subject of the experiments.

We kept both greenhouses at a constant temperature of 79 degrees Fahrenheit but set the relative humidity in one at 70 per cent and in the other at 40 per cent. The humidity apparently made no difference: the tomato plants grew at about the same rapid rate in both greenhouses. But we found that all the plants did rather poorly under the conditions we had established. They failed to develop a rich green color, were a little spindly and, worst of all, produced no fruits. From the several hundred plants we raised during the first year in these greenhouses we got only four ripe tomatoes!

Tomato-growing experts who saw the plants offered all sorts of explanations for the lack of fruit set, but none of their suggestions for changes in the culture of the plant helped. Finally we tried lowering the temperature of one of the greenhouses to 64 degrees F. The tomato plants in that greenhouse immediately started to set fruit, and it ripened normally. This seemed very strange, considering that tomatoes in the field grow and bear well at average temperatures much higher than the 79 degrees we had maintained in our greenhouses. We soon determined by experiments that the plants needed a daily cycle of temperature change, and that they did best if the night temperature (i.e., during the dark period of the plant's growth) was near 64 degrees.

It was plain that we needed much more detailed information to understand the effects of individual climatic factors on plants. The Earhart Foundation made a generous grant of $407,000 (to which it later added $74,000) for the construction and operation of a set of greenhouses in which all sorts of climatic factors can be controlled. This building, known as the Earhart Plant Research Laboratory, is popularly called the "phytotron" from *phyton* (the Greek word for plant) and *tron* (suggesting the contribution of physics to its remarkable equipment).

To give an idea of what the Earhart Laboratory is, let us make a quick tour through it. From the outside it looks like a big, pleasant house with large windows. But just inside the front door you are at once confronted with two doors, marked "Ladies" and "Gentlemen." Before you can enter the laboratory, you are required to go to a dressing room to wash your hands, comb your hair and change your street clothes for freshly laundered laboratory garments, to make sure that you will bring no insects or diseases into the laboratory.

Inside the building you find yourself in a remarkable atmosphere, free of any trace of insects, dust or smog. When you pass through the door into a greenhouse, you are suddenly in a new world, filled with plants on which a shimmering light plays. The shimmer is the result of water spraying on the glass roof, the purpose of the water being to absorb most of the sun's infrared radiation, which is not used in plant growth. The air feels perfectly fresh and pleasant, not muggy as in conventional greenhouses. Conditioned air circulates constantly throughout the greenhouse, entering through slots in the floor and leaving by ventilators in the walls. The air is completely replaced twice each minute. It removes most of the solar heat; at noon the greenhouse absorbs so much heat from the sun that during the half minute the circulating air spends in the room its temperature is raised by seven degrees. The ventilating system keeps the air moving so evenly that there are no stagnant spots, and all the plants within a greenhouse are subjected to exactly the same temperature and humidity.

The warmest greenhouse in the group is kept at 86 degrees during the day, summer and winter, but it does not feel too warm and is pleasant to walk in. You are, in fact, surprised to learn the actual air temperature. As every skier knows, the temperature of the air is less important, so far as the feeling of cold or warmth on our skin is concerned, than radiation. Moreover, the relative humidity of the air has a large influence on our perception of heat: dry air feels much cooler than humid air at the same temperature. And thirdly, air in motion feels cooler than quiet air at the same temperature.

A complete tour of the Earhart Laboratory would take us to 54 separate rooms where plants grow: individual greenhouses, darkrooms, artificially lighted compartments. All the plants stand on wheeled tables, so that they can easily be moved to any one of 54 different environments. We can combine a high daytime temperature with a high or low night temperature, vary the length of illumination, subject plants to artificial rain, to wind or to special gases. The particular variables that we manipulate in the laboratory are day temperature, night temperature, light intensity, duration of daily illumination, light quality, relative humidity of the air, wind, rain and gas content of the air. All other variables are excluded as much as possible, so that we can concentrate on the ones we have chosen. We keep the nutrition and soil conditions uniform by growing all the plants in vermiculite or gravel or a mixture of the two and watering them with a standard nutrient solution, which is piped into all greenhouses and growing-rooms. We can, of course, change the feeding of plants for special studies.

We grow many different plants together in the same greenhouse. Commercial growers generally use separate greenhouses for their different crop plants, each adjusted to the best growing conditions for its inhabitants. But our purpose is to test given plants under a wide variety of conditions. We may have tomatoes, peas, potatoes, African violets and a number of varieties of orchids all in the same greenhouse, measuring their various responses to the same temperature. In another greenhouse you may see desert plants growing next to coffee, barley, spinach, carnations and dozens of other plants—each in an experiment with different objectives.

Having walked through the greenhouses, let us look into the artificially lighted rooms. There are 13 groups of these, each serviced by a separate air conditioner. A group is divided into separate compartments by sliding doors, making it possible to keep plants in the different compartments at the same temperatures but under different light treatments. The plants are on tables of adjustable height, so that as they grow taller they can be kept at precisely the same distance from the light by lowering the table. Time clocks turn the lights on and off automatically. The plants can be wheeled into adjoining dark compartments on their trucks.

The temperature range in the artificially lighted rooms is from 38 to 86 degrees F.—a range which includes the temperature extremes at which tropical plants and alpine plants grow best. In the greenhouses we maintain day temperatures between 63 and 86 degrees and night temperatures between 53 and 73. The temperature is always lowered during the night, because most plants need this daily change to achieve their best growth.

When we come to the control and machinery areas, you will get a vivid idea of the complexity of the laboratory and the multiplicity of operations needed to keep it going. Located strategically in the center of the main floor is a control room with long panels covered with dials and recorders, showing exactly what the conditions are in every room. Here the superintendent of the building reigns over the controls, and here also the complicated administration to insure the best use of the growing space is carried out. In the basement we find labyrinths of air ducts and pipes for conveying hot and cold water, compressed air, nutrient solutions, deionized water, ordinary tap water and so on. There is a separate air conditioner for each of the rooms upstairs. Also in the basement are a general laboratory, shops, photographic rooms, etc.

One of the major problems that had to be solved to make the laboratory possible was filtering of the incoming air. Since much of the air conditioning is carried out through evaporative cooling, large volumes of air have to be taken into the building. All this air has to be filtered clean of dust, insects, disease spores and smog—no small matter in a city such as Pasadena where the air is contaminated with oxidation products of gasoline vapors which are toxic to plants. The capacity of our air-filtering system is approximately one ton of air per minute. Gradually all the difficulties involved in the filtering process were ironed out, and we now have completely clean air in the laboratory.

Now that we have looked over the laboratory, let us review some of the things that have been learned about plants and climate by experiments during its seven and one half years of operation. We shall start with the daily alternation of warm and cool temperatures that plants need, as we found in our original experiments with tomatoes. From extensions of those experiments we now know that most varieties of tomato plants require almost the same night temperature to set fruit. This explains why tomato production is usually very low in the tropics: the night temperatures there are above the optimal fruit-setting range. On the other hand, in cool climates the night temperatures are likely to be too low. The tomato yield is most reliable in California, where a relatively stable air mass during the summer insures fairly consistent night temperatures in the appropriate range. In areas such as the Southwest and the East, the great fluctuations in summer night temperatures make tomato production very variable. In some years there are only a few weeks of optimal night temperatures, and the crop is small. We are testing in our laboratory new varieties of tomatoes which breeders hope will tolerate a wider range of night temperatures, and indications are that the effort to breed a less sensitive tomato will be successful.

The potato plant, a close relative of the tomato, has in general the same temperature response; that is to say, it will form tubers only if the night temperatures fall within a rather narrow range. The optimal range is between 50 and 57 degrees F., about 10 degrees below the best range for tomatoes. This explains why the most successful potato-growing areas are mainly in the northern regions, such as Idaho, Maine, Ireland and northern Europe. In the central valley of California potatoes can be grown in the spring and late fall, but not during the middle of summer. In the tropics potato production is possible in the mountains, where the night temperatures are within the proper range. We have found that the important thing is the temperature to which the top of the potato plant is exposed: artificial heating or cooling of the soil has very little effect on the formation of tubers.

The response of sugar beets to temperature is somewhat more complicated. The plant grows best, at least in the case of warm-climate varieties, when the night temperature is about 68 degrees, but this is poor for sugar production. Sugar beets grown on a regime of 68-degree nights produce monstrous tubers with a very

51

low sugar content. They develop the highest sugar content when they are exposed to considerably lower night temperatures and also get comparatively little nitrogen nutrition. This suggests that the best sequence of conditions for beet sugar is a warm summer and early nitrogen feeding, while the plant is growing, followed by sunny autumn weather (for photosynthesis of sugar) with cold nights near freezing.

Peas and sweet peas grow mainly during the day and are little affected by the night temperature. They do best at daytime temperatures below 70 degrees; as soon as the regular daily temperature goes above 80 or 85 degrees, they start to die. In warm climates they can be grown only as winter crops.

The responses of a large number of other plants to day and night temperatures have been investigated, and for each of them an optimal range was established. Representative ranges for a few garden plants are shown in the chart opposite. As temperatures depart from the optimum, the growth of a plant becomes poorer and poorer, until it fails entirely. For example, African violets will die within weeks or months when they are kept continuously at the growing conditions which are best for the English daisy, whereas the English daisy dies when it is kept under the conditions best for the African violet. If we lay such a chart over a chart showing temperature variation at given localities we can tell which plants will grow where, and we can determine the most favorable growing season for each combination of plant and locality.

Most perennials of temperate climates depend upon cycles of temperature change. For instance, tulips will not flower in a completely even climate. There is a different optimal temperature for each successive stage of the plant's growth. First there must be a period of temperatures under 50 degrees to prepare for the growth of the flower stalk; the stalk then requires 63 degrees for its best growth; finally, if it is to produce new leaves and flowers in the following season, the tulip needs about 80 degrees. For the hya-

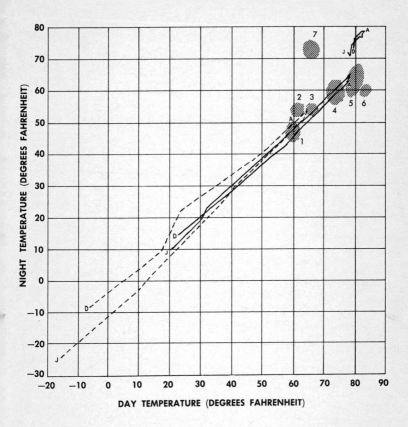

Optimum day and night temperatures for seven plants are indicated
by the shaded areas on this diagram. The plants are the English
daisy (1), stock (2), ageratum (3), China aster (4), zinnia
(5), petunia (6), African violet (7). The average day and night
temperatures for three locations are also plotted. The long
dashed curve plots the temperatures for Fairbanks, Alaska; the
black curve for Sioux Falls, S. D.; the short black curve at upper
right for San Juan, Puerto Rico. The letters on the curves indicate months of the year. Where the curve for a locality in-
tersects the shaded area for a plant, the plant will grow well.

53

cinth these requirements are all approximately 10 degrees higher. The onion starts its flowers at a low temperature, but it needs higher temperatures for other growth processes.

The biennial plants, such as beets, carrots and foxgloves, spend their first year making a rosette of leaves and a tap root which becomes filled with storage food. They are more or less dormant over the winter. Then in the following spring a long stem develops from the center of the rosette, and this produces flowers and fruits. They must have the cold winter period: if a beet, for instance, is kept instead at continuously high temperatures, it will live for years and grow to enormous size, but it will never form flowers.

Most of our deciduous trees also require a sequence of warm summers and cold winters. A peach or pear will not open its leaf or flower buds in the spring unless the tree has passed through a sufficiently cold winter. This chilling requirement has not been worked out in great detail, but in general it seems that the temperature must be below 40 degrees for several months. The requirement varies with the tree and the variety: the peach varieties that normally grow in cold climates require a longer period of low temperatures than peaches normally growing in warmer climates. Thus a peach that does well in the St. Louis area will not leaf out in southern California, whereas a southern California peach transplanted to St. Louis is apt to sprout during a warm spell in the middle of winter because its moderate cold requirement has been fulfilled too soon.

The deciduous trees are controlled by climate in two ways: by changes in the temperature and by changes in the length of the day [see "The Control of Flowering," by Aubrey W. Naylor, on page 14]. A peach or pear tree senses the approach of autumn through the decrease in day length; its buds then begin to go into the dormant state. If a peach tree is kept continuously on long days in the laboratory, it will go on growing vegetatively without

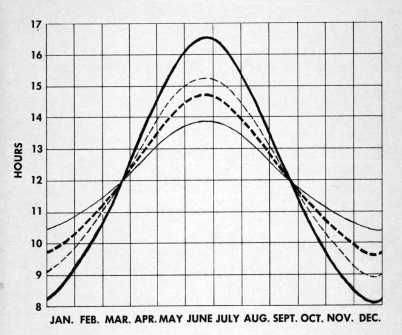

HOURS

17 16 15 14 13 12 11 10 9 8

JAN. FEB. MAR. APR. MAY JUNE JULY AUG. SEPT. OCT. NOV. DEC.

Length of the day determines when plants flower. The vertical co-
ordinate of this diagram is the length of the day in hours and
minutes; the horizontal co-ordinate, the months of the year. The
four curves depict the annual change in the length of the day at
four latitudes: that of Miami (26 degrees North), that of San
Francisco (37 degrees), that of Chicago (42 degrees) and that of
Winnipeg (50 degrees). The cocklebur requires 9 hours or more
of darkness (*i.e.*, 15 hours or less of light) in order to flower.
Thus in Winnipeg it has a long period of vegetative growth even
after it is ripe to flower. In Miami, however, it flowers immediately when it is ripe to do so. In Winnipeg the buds of the cocklebur appear on about August 3, so late that frost will probably
kill the plants.

55

forming resting buds. In nature the sequence of long days, short days, cold temperatures and warm temperatures synchronizes the peach tree with the progression of seasons. The tree's response is complex. Two successive cold winters, separated by a warm summer, are needed—the first for the initiation of new flower buds during the following summer and the second to prepare for the flowering of these buds.

Warm-climate evergreen shrubs such as camellias also have a dual control by seasonal fluctuations in temperature and day length. In their case the flower buds are formed during high summer temperatures and the flowers open during the next winter. For vegetative growth they must have long days. Therefore camellias do well only when subjected to sufficient seasonal variations.

Many tropical plants, e.g., palms and hibiscus, develop leaves and flowers all the year around. The reason they cannot be grown in a temperate climate is that their vegetative growths would be killed by frost. Yet even some tropical plants, such as the royal poinciana, respond to a yearly cycle—namely, the cycle of rainy and dry seasons.

Obviously climate exerts its influence upon plants by affecting their biochemistry. Concerning this we do not yet have much specific information. But we do find definite effects of climatic factors upon the taste and other qualities of fruits. Using the tongue as an analytical instrument, we have investigated the influences of various factors upon the flavor of strawberries.

When strawberry plants are grown in warm or moderate temperatures, the fruits are red, sweet and slightly acid, but they have no strawberry flavor! To develop flavor they must ripen at daytime temperatures of about 50 degrees. By various experiments we learned that the plants have to be exposed to the right light and temperature conditions for at least a week to acquire the full strawberry aroma.

These results explain why generally the first strawberries of the season taste best. They ripen while the early morning temperature is about 50 degrees. Later in the spring and during the summer the strawberry crop is practically without aroma, because the ripening fruit does not receive the proper temperature at any time during the day. At high altitudes, or far north, low morning temperatures occur even during summer, and strawberries from Alaska, northern Sweden or the high Rockies taste marvelous at any time.

With this information it should be possible to grow strawberries deliberately under conditions in which full flavor develops, producing a product of reproducibly high quality. For it is after all the flavor for which we pay 40 cents a basket; the amount of sugar and acid contained in a basket of strawberries (if bought separately) would be worth less than one cent.

It is possible that in many other fruits the same factors are important for flavor development. Probably the excellent taste of northern apples is due to the low temperatures during the last days of ripening, especially in the morning. Breeders of fruit give the main emphasis to its keeping quality and appearance, but growers ought to pay as much attention to flavor, which is the basis on which we buy fruits in the first place. With more experiments we may obtain knowledge of the conditions under which flavor can be developed most effectively.

Since agriculture is the backbone of our existence, and since climate is a decisive factor in crop production, what can we do about it? This is a problem of such magnitude that it certainly should occupy many of our best brains, and research and development groups in agroclimatology should be active all over the world. Every agricultural experiment station and agricultural college has groups of scientists studying plant diseases and pests, breeding new varieties, determining proper soil treatments, developing agricultural implements and machinery. But only a few places have research teams in agroclimatology. Among these are the Drexel Institute of Technology's Research Laboratory of Climatology, the Department of Agronomy at the University of Wisconsin and the College of Agriculture at the University of California.

Such a team should comprise meteorologists, climatologists, agriculturists and plant physiologists. A phytotron of the kind we have at Cal Tech is a necessary instrument for the investigation. Now that the need for such a laboratory has been recognized, we can expect that in the near future a number will be built, not only for basic research but also for the solution of many problems in agriculture, horticulture and forestry.

Not much can be done about improving the selection of climate for the great staple crops, such as wheat, rice and cotton, for these crops are already generally grown in the most favorable areas, as a result of experience, economic forces (the profit margin is narrow) and the development of varieties adapted to local conditions. The specialty crops, on the other hand, are tried everywhere, with more or less (usually less) success. Agroclimatology can advise as to whether such crops are likely to succeed in a given locality and which varieties are the best to plant.

It can also be helpful with weather warnings. One of the best examples is the frost warning system for citrus growers in southern California. During the winter farmers receive a daily report by radio on the expected minimum temperature in each area. They are told at what hour temperatures will drop to the point where their orchard heaters need to be fired. This service is so reliable that farmers know when they can sleep soundly through the night and when they must organize crews to light the heaters. In the Netherlands the Meteorological Institute has an efficient warning service against outbreaks of potato blight. It tells potato growers when the climatic factors threaten spread of the disease, so that they can spray their fields with Bordeaux mixture in time.

Similar warning services are being developed for many other farming operations. For instance, calculations of the rate of water loss by the soil make it possible to tell farmers when and how much they must irrigate their fields. If reliable long-range weather forecasting can be developed, whole new possibilities will open up for agroclimatology. Experts will then be able to recommend what varieties of a plant (e.g., tomato) should be planted for the best yield.

There are already a number of ways in which farmers can control climatic factors in the field to some extent. They can accelerate the flowering of chrysanthemums and other plants by means of electric lights or curtains which artificially regulate the day length. We have found that it is possible to induce tomato plants to set fruit as early as May or June in Pasadena by covering them with dark cloth during the late afternoon, when the temperature is in the proper range for fruit set. These plants start to form tomatoes at least a month ahead of uncovered plants. A more inexpensive way to obtain early fruit set is to plant the tomatoes along the east side of a wall or a shade tree, so that they are shaded and start their night activities early in the evening, while the temperature is still high enough.

As we learn more about plant responses to climate, we undoubtedly will find more ways to control their growth, and it is a comforting thought that technology is so advanced in our present world that almost any technical problem can be solved if it is urgent enough.

We have considered the possibilities of adjusting climate to plants; to what extent can we adjust plants to a climate? There is very little scientific evidence to support the idea that over the course of time a given variety of plant can become acclimated to conditions for which it is not originally suited. The soundest scheme is to attempt to breed new varieties which are fitted to the climate. This of course has been tried by many plant breeders and in many experiment stations. Every state of the Union has an experiment station with its own breeding program seeking to adapt cereals and other plants to the particular climatic conditions in that state. One of the great difficulties in these breeding programs is that there are minor differences in climate from year to year. The plants selected in one year may not be appropriate for typical conditions.

With the phytotron, in which the critical climatic factors can be controlled, it should be possible to select varieties which are specifically adjusted to particular climates. We are conducting such a program at the present time to breed tomato plants which will set fruit at comparatively high night temperatures in places such as Texas; the research program is financed by the Campbell Soup Company, the largest single grower of tomatoes in the U. S. Starting with varieties which are able to set at high temperatures but produce inferior tomatoes, we have found that by cross-breeding we can transfer their high-temperature tolerance to good tomato varieties. By such breeding it should be possible to develop a series of forms suitable for different climates.

The examples discussed in this article should make it clear that a great future lies ahead for the field of agroclimatology. The Earhart Laboratory has already shown in a number of cases that experiments under carefully controlled conditions can greatly cut down the expense of field testing. For example, it has assisted the United States Forest Service in selecting cover plants which are likely to grow well on mountainsides in southern California. In another project we found that the herb called the American hellebore (*Veratrum viride*), which had failed in all field experiments, needed six months of freezing temperatures followed by six months of very cool weather. The plant was then tried at high elevations in the mountains of northern Washington and it grew successfully there. In these cases climate turned out to be the most important selective factor, and this is probably true of many plants.

Basically the most important climatic factor that man seeks to put to use in agriculture is the energy of sunlight. Our present methods capture only a small part of the available energy. Laboratory experiments show that a plant can convert 10 per cent or more of the incident light energy into chemical energy in the form of its organic products. But in practice we harvest as plant material no more than 2 per cent of the solar energy that falls on a field of, say, corn or sugar beets. One reason for this relative inefficiency is that an annual, starting anew from seed, covers only a small percentage of the surface of the field in the early part of the season. Perennial crop plants provide more coverage and absorb more solar energy over the season, but most of their production goes into unusable leaves and branches.

Obviously these facts offer a vast field of research for students of climate and plant production. The objectives must be to get better coverage of the earth's surface with plants and to improve the efficiency of conversion of sunlight into chemical energy. Already it has been found that algae in a nutrient solution can transform light into organic energy two or three times more efficiently than the higher plants. However, a rather elaborate setup is needed to cultivate algae effectively; the expenditure of an equal amount of ingenuity and technological effort could make the higher plants just as efficient in absorbing the sun's energy.

Climate is one of our major natural resources. By learning exactly what the relationships are between climatic factors and plants we should be able to make far greater use of this resource.

PART 3 GROWTH AND FORM

I. THE GROWTH OF MUSHROOMS
by John Tyler Bonner

A Princeton University biologist, John Tyler Bonner specializes in the study of very simple organisms, especially slime molds. He was a junior fellow at Harvard University and for his Ph.D. he did research on fungi under William H. Weston. Since 1947 he has been teaching at Princeton as an associate professor of biology.

II. LEAF SHAPE
by Eric Ashby

Now President and Vice-Chancellor of The Queen's University, Belfast, Sir Eric Ashby finds himself transformed from scientist to educator. As an undergraduate of the Imperial College of Science, London, in the 1920s, his aim was a career in physics. Under the influence of Sir John Farmer, however, his energies were deflected into botany. He did distinguished and original work, reflecting his first love, in the mathematical analysis of growth and in the application of statistical methods to plant ecology. At 33, he was called to the University of Sydney, in Australia, as head of the department of botany. There his scientific work was interrupted for the first time by the war. He served as chairman of the Australian National Research Council and then for a time as Minister at the Australian Legation in Moscow. At the end of the war he returned to England and to science at the University of Manchester. Ashby received his present appointment in 1950 and was knighted in 1956. His principal concern today is with the problems of science education; his hobbies are mountaineering, especially in the Austrian Alps, and chamber music, as a faithful member of a string quartet.

III. TISSUE CULTURES

by Philip R. White

Recognized as the perfector of techniques for plant cell culture, Philip White is a member of the research staff of the Roscoe B. Jackson Memorial Laboratory at Bar Harbor, Maine. He grew up on a Montana farm and went to the University of Montana, where botany, the viola (which he now plays with the Bangor Little Symphony Orchestra) and a literary bent competed for his attention. After a year of teaching English in a school in France, he decided on a career in botany. With a Ph.D. from Johns Hopkins, in 1928, he went to work for the U. S. Department of Agriculture and then the United Fruit Co. and held research appointments at the Boyce Thompson Institute and the University of Berlin before he settled down to his important work at the Rockefeller Institute in Princeton, New Jersey. There, over a 13-year period, he developed his techniques for plant-tissue culture and, with his colleague Armin Braun, first demonstrated the existence of true cancers in plants. Some of his cultures are now in their 21st year of continuous cultivation. White has spent the past decade in developing similar techniques for the culture of animal and human tissues.

THE GROWTH OF MUSHROOMS

by John Tyler Bonner

THERE ARE many ways to study how living things grow, and the study of mushrooms may seem at first thought one of the least promising. I had always been dimly aware that mushrooms grow, but the idea that they might be a suitable subject for investigation of the growth process never crossed my mind until I encountered an unusual instance at Woods Hole, Mass., where we were spending the summer. I used to walk our dog every morning over an abandoned asphalt road, and one day I noticed some round bulges the size of a butter plate in the asphalt. A few mornings later I saw to my utter amazement that one of the mounds had erupted and a mushroom had pushed up through the pavement. My first thought was: What a remarkable feat of strength for a delicate mushroom! A good friend politely informed me that it was not only strength but also persistence, for asphalt is actually a liquid, and a steady force will move it. It turned out that I had by no means been the first to observe such a phenomenon: in fact, I found in a U.S.S.R. journal a paper describing a similar eruption on the floor of a Soviet factory—which I suspect must have kept the NKVD busy for quite some time.

It is surprising how little literature there is on the details of mushroom growth. As is often the case, the earliest accounts are the most comprehensive. Few facts have been added to the classic report by the nineteenth-century Strasbourg botanist Anton de

Bary. Teachers of botany today have a great deal to say about the growth of the onion root tip and other advanced members of the plant kingdom, but they ignore the mushroom—it "just grows."

Mushrooms are encountered by most people only as a garnish for steaks. The kind you buy at the supermarket is a cultivated variety of the common field mushroom *Agaricus campestris*. Whether you are a housewife who has washed it for cooking, or a consumer who has poked at it with a fork, you know that a mushroom is composed of an umbrella-shaped dome capping a thick stalk. If you have ever taken one apart, you probably also know that, smooth and sleek as the object seems, the mushroom is actually a compacted mass of minute, cotton-like threads, and that its roots are delicate filaments spread widely through the soil.

The mushroom is in essence a spore-bearing and spore-distributing structure. Cells on the fluted undersurface of the cap shed tiny spores which are carried off by the wind. The spore output of a single mushroom is staggering—as many as half a million spores a minute for a period of three or four days. Break the cap off the stem, place it on a sheet of paper and you will be rewarded with a pretty showered pattern of spores out-lining the fluted gills of the undersurface. A botanist identifies the species of mushroom by the color of the spores.

In a suitable environment—soil, compost, rotten wood or any other nourishing medium—the spores will send out filaments that invade every nook and cranny. Like the spores themselves, these young filaments contain half the number of chromosomes of adult mushroom cells. In essence they are gametes, like sperm and egg. To develop they must meet and fuse. We cannot, however, call them male and female, for most mushroom varieties have four "sexes." Among the four there are only two possible cross-matings —i.e., one and three, two and four.

After a pair of filaments has fused, combining in the cell nuclei the normal double complement of chromosomes, it continues to sop up food, to elongate, advance and invade. The thread grows at its tip, and as the nuclei divide, transverse walls are formed across the filament. In the end, however, the cross walls are perforated with holes that form a passage along the length of the thread, through which protoplasm and even nuclei can pass freely from one cell to the next. This flow was studied carefully by the late Reginald Buller, a distinguished Canadian botanist, and was found to be important for the growth of the mushroom.

A network of growing filaments, called a mycelium, spreads through the soil like the ripples from a stone dropped into a quiet pond. As I sit writing, I can see in the lawn below my fourth-story window a circular patch about six feet across in which the grass has a slightly fresher, greener appearance. I know that the area is underlain by a mushroom mycelium. Last fall the patch was ringed by a perfect circle of mushrooms—what is known as a "fairy ring." Such a ring starts at the center; as the plant's roots deplete the soil of mushroom food, the mushrooms move outward in an ever expanding circle, forming a perfect ring so long as the weather conditions satisfy the fruiting and growth requirements. John Ramsbottom, former Keeper of Botany at the British Museum in London, has a chapter on fairy rings in his delightful book *Mushrooms and Toadstools.* In one year the ring of the "fairy-ring mushroom" (*Marasmius oreades*) will advance five to 19 inches, and from this it can be calculated that certain large patches must be from 400 to 600 years old. Ramsbottom caps this bit of information with a remarkable aerial photograph of plainly visible fairy rings surrounding the famous Stonehenge ruins.

Cultivated mushrooms are grown in a rich compost of soil and horse manure. Many seed companies offer spawn (young mycelia) for planting with fairly complete directions. A tray of compost with spawn should be kept in a damp, quiet place at a temperature near 65 degrees Fahrenheit. A cave or old-fashioned cellar makes an admirable mushroom-growing chamber. In a matter of a few months the flat will be completely interlaced with the white mycelium. The first inkling of fruiting will be the appearance of small white pinpoints all over the surface. Some of these begin to enlarge (the rest appear to be inhibited by the faster-growing ones). When a shoot has grown to a height of about five millimeters, the mushroom cap and stalk begin to be distinguishable. The mushroom expands in both thickness and height until it is 15 to 20 millimeters tall; thereafter it grows in height only. As it shoots up, the cap eventually unfolds from the stem like the opening of an umbrella.

When I embarked on the project of studying this process in more detail at Princeton University about a year ago, two seniors, Raphael H. Levey and K. Kent Kane, decided that they would like to take part, and they energetically set out to find a source of supply. Before long they had located a mushroom grower, Karl Knaust of Catskill, New York, who generously agreed to supply us with all the material we needed. It seemed to me a rather distant source, but then I discovered that its proximity to Vassar College made it attractive to my associates. They made frequent week-end trips and returned with prepared flats of compost. It was then a matter of finding a suitable place for lodging the flats, and we ended up by placing them under various laboratory tables in cool rooms.

The first step was to measure the relative growth of different parts of the young mushroom. We marked the stalk at equal intervals up its length with dots of vivid red carmine dye—an old trick—and then periodically photographed and measured the developments. Any student of mushroom growth knows that the stalk grows in a peculiar preferential manner: its elongation takes place mainly in a region just below the cap. We were interested in measuring the exact extent of growth in this and other zones at different stages.

The dye spots told a graphic story. Along most of the stalk the spots remained round, but a spot placed within a certain sharply

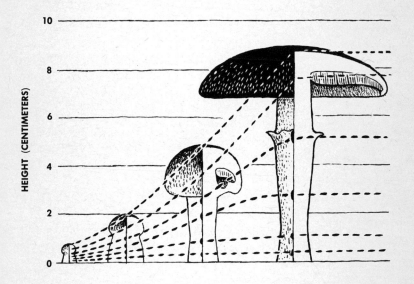

Positions of spots on the stem of the growing mushroom trace curves that show the changes in the plant's proportions and the different rates of growth of its various parts. The relative elongation of the spots is another indication of the same developments. The right-hand side of the mushroom is sectioned in each stage to show the changes in its internal structure.

defined zone next to the cap would stretch out into a vertical line —here the stalk grew (see drawing on preceding page). The cap also grew somewhat unevenly, but not in any such abrupt fashion: it grew fastest at the edge and gradually slower toward the center.

So from these dye experiments it is clear that once a mushroom 15 to 20 millimeters high begins to expand, the stalk does so only at a restricted zone below the cap and the cap does so in a gradient, highest at the edge. Before the incipient mushroom has reached that height, all parts of it expand at a uniform rate.

We put some marked young mushrooms in a moist chamber without soil, and we sliced others vertically through the cap and stalk, as one might slice them for cooking: these, too, expanded in the same regions where growth occurred in mushrooms growing normally in soil—though their expansion was quite limited. We even found that the stalk's growth zone alone, dissected from the stalk and placed on moist agar jelly, expanded appreciably.

It soon became obvious that to make any progress in understanding the growth mechanics we would have to study the development of the filaments that make up the mushroom. We took mushrooms at different stages of growth, treated them in the usual way for tissue examination under the miscroscope, cut them into thin sections after embedding them in paraffin wax, and then put them on slides, stained them with suitable dyes and examined the filaments through the microscope. We did not discover any startling new facts, but we did find it possible to correlate the mushroom's external expansion with changes in the arrangement of its internal threads.

Until the button is about four millimeters high, the filaments are bunched in a most irregular tangle. As it grows slightly taller, some orientation begins to appear in the stalk just below the cap: the filaments here start to line up parallel to one another. By the time the button has reached 10 millimeters in height, this orientation in the upper stalk region is complete. The rest of the stalk remains a tangled mass of threads, and the cap also looks tangled, although occasionally one can see some radial orientation.

We have good evidence that after the mushroom has reached a height of 15 to 20 millimeters the cells of the stalk cease dividing and the filaments stop increasing in number. Thereafter, it appears, all the further rapid growth in height of the mushroom is due to mere elongation of the cells themselves. One evidence of this is given by comparative measurements of changes in height and thickness; another by measurements of weight. The height of the stalk increases in direct proportion to the weight, which shows that all the increase of substance must go into the elongation of filaments.

What intake feeds the elongation of the cells: is it merely water or is it other material from the soil as well? This question was tested simply by comparing the wet with the dry weights of a whole series of mushrooms at different stages. It was found that the dry weight increased in direct proportion to the wet weight, so the cells must be swelled by solid materials along with the water. This fact undoubtedly accounts for the relatively slight expansion found in isolated pieces of mushroom placed in a moist chamber, where only water intake is possible.

From all this one can see that the shape and future of a mushroom are mapped in the very early stages of its growth. Its intertwining threads are sorted out in the stalk in their proper locations and even in the correct number—all ready for the big push of growth. Then if the external conditions are favorable, there will be a sudden surge of materials from the soil mycelia upward into the mushroom, and its cells will elongate so that the mushroom can shoot into the air. There is then in the button a preformed pattern which, like an unfilled balloon, merely needs the proper filling substance to blow it up. This undoubtedly accounts for the proverbial fact that many kinds of mushrooms pop up suddenly. The buttons are often hidden below the grass or leaves, and as soon as the temperature and moisture conditions are just right, the final process of the upward movement of materials inside the threads can take place with dramatic speed. The gun, to change the metaphor, is carefully loaded, and all parts of the primordium are arranged in their proper number and place. Then the rains and the temperature pull the trigger that sets the mushroom off on its final spurt of growth.

LEAF SHAPE

by Eric Ashby

THE exciting thing about scientific research is not reviewing the results; it is making the observations. Unhappily this pleasure is no longer readily accessible to the amateur in these days of cyclotrons and infrared spectrometers; in such esoteric sciences as physics and chemistry he must be content with reading accounts of experiments he could not possibly have done himself. But in biology it is still possible for an acute observer to make interesting discoveries with no more equipment than any house and garden can provide. Indeed, we can begin to study a fundamental biological phenomenon, the aging of plants, with the simplest of observations—the sizes and shapes of leaves.

If you observe carefully the shapes of successive leaves on the stem of almost any annual plant, you will be struck by something you may not have noticed before: no two leaves on the stem are alike. Carrot, delphinium, morning-glory, hibiscus, cosmos, sugar beet—all these and most other plants show changes in shape from leaf to leaf up the stem. And the differences are not haphazard. In delphinium, for instance, there is a progressive increase in the number of segments in each succeeding leaf. If the first leaf has nine segments, the second has 12, the third 18. In morning-glory the first three or four leaves may be shaped like a heart; the subsequent leaves are more and more deeply lobed. In the English harebell the first-formed leaves are round; later-formed leaves are narrow and grasslike. In many plants the changes are so regular

73

that they may be plotted as a graph, with leaf number along one axis and some measure of leaf shape along the other axis, as shown in the graph of changes in the shape of cotton leaves on the opposite page.

Closer inspection discloses other striking differences between one leaf and the next. Under the microscope the surface of a leaf appears as a tessellated pavement of cells, each about one 500,-000th of a square inch in area. There are about four million such cells on the surface of an ordinary beet or tobacco leaf. Now, the size of these cells diminishes from leaf to leaf up the stem, so that upper leaves have smaller cells than lower leaves, and they also have fewer cells—there are fewer tiles in the pavement and the tiles are smaller. This means, of course, that the upper leaves as a whole are smaller.

What is the importance of these observations on the shape and size of successive leaves up a stem? What sort of biological hypothesis can we derive from them? The observations have scientific significance for two reasons. In the first place they provide a simple quantitative example of a pattern in time: as the plant grows older the leaves it produces change in a measurable manner. The hereditary constitution of the plant does not change, yet the patterns produced by the hereditary constitution do change. In this respect an organism is similar to a piece of music, developing variations on a theme. In the second place these changes in pattern may be a way of measuring the elusive process called physiological aging. The round leaves in the common harebell, for instance, are called juvenile leaves. Under ordinary conditions adult plants do not form such leaves. But a plant kept in a state of delayed development by deep shade and high moisture, or a plant grown from a cutting, often does form juvenile leaves, even though it is an adult plant; and under these conditions flowering and old age are delayed. Is it possible, then, that leaf shape will provide some measure of the stage of development reached by a plant—not its time-age, but its physiological age? Any such possibility deserves careful attention.

From our initial observations, therefore, we are driven to ask how and why upper leaves on annual plants differ from lower

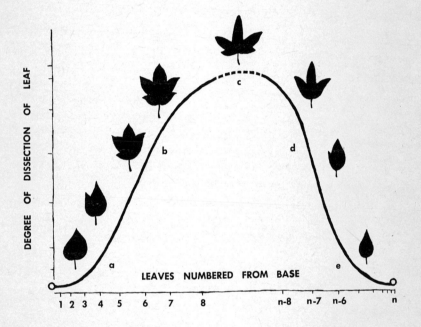

The shapes of leaves in a cotton plant vary as the plant waxes and wanes. The first leaves of the young plant at left are smooth-edged single lobes. Midway in the life cycle, the leaves are sharply dissected. The last leaves put out by the aging plant resemble the first.

75

leaves. In such an inquiry it is well to begin with the simplest hypothesis. The simplest hypothesis is that upper leaves differ from lower leaves merely because they develop later in the season, and that the consistent changes in shape and size merely reflect the changes in temperature and light from spring to summer.

It is not difficult to test this hypothesis. If, for instance, morning-glory plants are sown in pots once a week through the spring, and all are grown side by side in the same greenhouse, then the tenth leaf of an early sowing will develop at the same time and under the same environmental conditions as, say, the second leaf of a late sowing. If the leaf shape and size are merely the product of the environment, these tenth and second leaves should be alike. Results of numerous experiments show unambiguously that this is not the case. Leaf shape and size depend mainly upon position on the plant. It is true that they are also influenced by the season, but the effects of season are quite different from the effects of the position of the leaf on the plant. We are therefore obliged to reject the simplest hypothesis, and to seek an explanation of the trends in leaf shape and size in some internal change in the plant related to its physiological age.

We must note at once that the aging of a plant is quite different from that of an animal. In an animal the processes of growth occur all over the body until maturity, and the animal may then continue to live a long time even though growth has stopped. In a plant the processes of growth are localized at the growing tips of the stems. In a corn plant, for example, cells at the tip are continually dividing to form new leaves. Above the youngest leaves there always remains a zone of newly formed cells, called the meristem, from which subsequent growth will come. The manner of growth of a corn plant from its tip is, to use a far-fetched analogy, rather like the growth of a knitted woolen sock from the needles at one end. It follows, therefore, that a plant is not the same age all over; its lower leaves may be three or four months old while the uppermost leaf is only a few hours old. So long as the plant is growing, new meristem cells are being formed at the tip of the stem.

Thus in time-age the tip is perpetually young. But it is certainly not perpetually young in physiological age. In a young plant the meristem cells give rise to juvenile leaves; in an older plant they give rise to adult leaves and eventually to flowers. And it appears that this inexorable process of aging goes on even when the plant has a constant supply of nutrients and constant conditions of light.

So we meet here a central problem of biology: the problem of the cause of old age. There are encouraging signs that the anatomy and shape of leaves may be a useful measure of plant aging—and to be able to measure a phenomenon is the first step toward understanding it.

Recently at the University of Manchester we have begun to study the aging of a plant under constant environmental conditions. The plant we use is the common floating duckweed, which can be found in almost any stagnant pond. Each leaflike frond produces a "daughter" frond from a pocket in its side; when this first daughter is fully grown, a second daughter frond is produced from a similar pocket in the other side of the parent. By the time the second daughter is grown the first daughter frond has broken away and become a separate plant, and out of the empty pocket a third daughter appears. This is followed by a fourth daughter in the pocket formerly occupied by the second daughter. In this way a mother frond may bring forth up to five daughter fronds, after which the mother frond dies. The life expectation of a mother frond is about 45 days. The five daughter fronds produced in this time are similar to five leaves on a normal plant.

The remarkable fact is that even in the most carefully controlled artificial environment each of the daughter fronds is smaller than the one before, so that the fourth and fifth daughters are less than half the size of the first daughter. To put it another way, the meristem cells of the mother frond are, as it were, "running down."

In terms of physiology, there are two possible explanations for the running down of a frond. The first is that the mother frond produces a growth-stimulating substance which is gradually used up, so that the fifth frond receives much less than the first frond. The second possible explanation is that the mother frond produces a growth-inhibiting substance which, as it accumulates, restricts the growth of successive daughter fronds more and more.

A simple experiment shows which of these explanations is the more likely. We cut out an immature daughter frond from its mother. If its mother supplied a stimulating substance, the separated daughter frond, deprived of this substance, should be abnormally small when it matures. If its mother supplied an inhibiting substance, the freed frond should grow abnormally large. It turns out that when such a surgical operation is performed, the excised daughter frond never grows to its normal size; it is always abnormally small. This indicates that a mother frond stimulates the growth of a daughter frond, and the reduction in size of successive daughter fronds may be due to a diminution in its supply of growth-stimulating substance.

But that is not the entire story. If it were, then successive generations in a colony of duckweed plants would become smaller and smaller and ultimately disappear. This does not happen; indeed the average size of fronds in a colony remains about the same. The reason is that the impoverished fourth or fifth daughter fronds reverse the trend and produce "granddaughter" fronds that are larger than themselves. The process of aging during the life of a frond is followed by a process of rejuvenation. Each new frond in a duckweed colony is in fact part of a cycle of aging and rejuvenation. Physiological age, unlike time-age, can be put into reverse.

This cycle appears in its most familiar form in annual plants, which "run down" and die each year but leave behind seeds whose germination is in effect a revival of youth. We see in the duckweed, however, a case of rejuvenation without seed formation.

Our data are still much too slim to justify a general theory of senescence and rejuvenescence in plants. We must be content with rough working hypotheses, most of which are unsatisfactory. The interpretation we have been considering, which is not so much a hypothesis as an attempt at diagnosis, was put forward by a Russian botanist, N. P. Krenke, who died in 1940. Krenke had observed that the leaves of some varieties of cotton change shape from place to place up the stem. Successive leaves become more and more deeply lobed, and then the process reverses and succeeding ones become less and less lobed. If lobing occurs in a comparatively early leaf, then flowering also occurs early, and vice versa. Krenke therefore suggested that the cycle of leaf shape in cotton is a measure of physiological age. He suggested also that when a side branch arises from a bud on the main stem, the branch exhibits some degree of rejuvenation, for it repeats the shape sequence found on the main stem. The repetition is not perfectly parallel: for instance, a side branch from a bud low on the stem has its first leaf slightly less lobed than the leaf on the main stem, while a side branch high on the stem has its first leaf slightly more lobed than the leaf on the main stem. This, however, is precisely what one would expect if leaf shape measured physiological age, and if all side branches were, like the granddaughter fronds of duckweed, physiologically younger than the main stem at the place where they arise. Since lobing in this plant at first is a sign of age and later becomes a sign of youth, we would expect the high side branches to exhibit their greater youth by developing more deeply lobed leaves.

Krenke's hypothesis does not, of course, *explain* these consistent changes; it does not even describe all types of such change. But it is a bold and provocative idea which stimulates further work, and it convinces us that the analysis of leaf shape may become a problem of great importance in biology.

TISSUE CULTURES
by Philip R. White

Every cell of the body has a dual character. First there is a fundamental character which arises from the innate qualities of the cell itself; this cannot be altered without destroying the cell. Then there is a more ephemeral character which arises from the fact that the cell is embedded in a complex environment which includes millions of other body cells; this can be changed without necessarily destroying the cell. The first qualities are personal, so to speak, the second social.

So long as a cell remains in its normal place in the body it is difficult or impossible to distinguish between its personal and social qualities. If, however, a cell or group of cells is removed from its usual surroundings and placed in an environment which, though asocial, is sufficient for survival, the social aspects of its character fall away, and we can discover not only what is the real individuality of the cell, but also just how the social factors have affected it. Cells or tissues so isolated are called tissue cultures.

If a piece of willow twig a foot long is stuck into moist sand, it will sprout roots at one end and leaves at the other, finally growing into a new tree. If we divide the one-foot piece into six two-inch pieces, each piece will sprout roots and leaves in the same manner. Some of the tissues that were near the "base" of the longer piece, and would have produced roots there, will in the basal two-inch bit now find themselves at the top of the smaller piece, and will produce leaves instead. In other words, the development these cells have undergone is an expression of their social relationships to the functional whole.

If, however, we take only a very small bit of tissue, either from the interior of the tip of a young stem or from the rapidly growing layer between the wood and bark (the layer that splits when one makes a willow whistle), the requirements for survival and the results will be quite different. On sand alone such a bit would soon die. To nurse the tissue we place it on a nutrient medium that contains all the salts, carbohydrates, vitamins and other substances needed for growth. On such a nutrient the cells will multiply without forming roots, leaves or bark. They develop into an unformed mass which can be kept growing for months or years. This, then, is a tissue culture. By reducing the number and variety of cells that can affect any given cell in the mass, we have removed most of its social environment and permitted the cells to express only their innate characteristics. This mass can be divided into a large number of cultures, all with identical heredity and identical environmental background. We call a group of cultures so derived a clone of tissues. Their personal characters are all exactly alike, and they can be manipulated to determine precisely those variants of nutrient, temperature, acidity and the like that are needed to elicit roots or leaves or woody deposits or what one will.

This sounds very simple, but in practice the problem of establishing the necessary techniques, particularly of defining the nutritional requirements, proved far from simple. Nutrition as a science is relatively new. Forty years of experiments elapsed between the first carefully planned attack on the problem, begun in 1898 by Gottlieb Haberlandt of Germany, and its solution. In 1939 three independent workers—Roger J. Gautheret at the Sorbonne in Paris, Pierre Nobécourt at the University of Grenoble, France, and the author at the Rockefeller Institute for Medical Research in Princeton, New Jersey—almost simultaneously published accounts of the first really successful cultures. These three publications laid a firm foundation for the study of plant tissue

culture. In the past decade, the results of these studies have blos-
somed into an important experimental discipline.

What nutrients does a piece of plant tissue need for growth?
Let us make the experiment with a thin slice cut through the
young stem of a tomato plant. When placed on moist sand or on
gelatin saturated with water, this tissue, assuming that it is kept
free of molds, will undergo a characteristic series of changes. If it
is large enough, it may form roots and stem growing points as did
our willow. More likely it will merely swell. The surface cells
will take up water and expand into large sacs or vesicles. Some
cells below the surface will divide parallel to the direction of the
cut, and the new-formed cells will be transformed into cork. The
interior cells will become woody and the mass will soon cease to
grow. Here it is evident that our substituted environment, which
of course is not a nutrient, is far from adequate for anything like
normal function.

We know that isolated roots can be made to grow for years on
a relatively simple nutrient containing only certain salts, cane
sugar, thiamin and one or more other special substances, which
differ with the particular root studied. In the case of tomato roots
the special supplement required is either glycine, the simplest of
all the amino acids, or the two vitamins pyridoxine and niacin. It
would be logical to suppose that stem tissues, as well as roots,
would grow on one of these nutrients. Unfortunately this has not
proved to be the case. Stem tissues require something more.
Gautheret and Nobécourt have shown that this something more
is the "plant hormone," or auxin, named indole-acetic acid. Indole-
acetic acid is extremely poisonous in above-normal amounts; indeed, its near-relative, 2, 4-D, is a deadly weed-killer. But in very
low concentrations it possesses important growth-stimulating
properties. When added to the nutrient of an isolated bit of tissue
in a concentration of about one part in 100 million, it suppresses
the formation of cork and wood, promotes cell division and causes

the fragment to grow, somewhat irregularly to be sure, but nevertheless continuously. Thus indole-acetic acid permits the establishment of "tissue cultures."

For many plants a related substance, naphthalene-acetic acid, is somewhat more satisfactory. Some tissues may require additional foods, such as biotin, pantothenic acid, inositol or other vitamins. But for the majority of tissues studied to date, indole-acetic acid or its equivalent is the only indispensable supplement to the basic nutrient.

With the establishment of these relatively simple requirements, many different plant materials have been grown and studied during the past few years. The first plant investigated was the carrot. Carrot tissues grown in the dark require thiamin, but when exposed to light they synthesize their own thiamin. Carrot cultures at first possess a distinct polarity, but this is lost after four or five passages, i.e., divisions of the multiplying cells and their transfer to fresh nutrient. They also lose their capacity to form roots. Gautheret found that after long cultivation some carrot tissues even lost their requirement for indole-acetic acid; they acquired the capacity to synthesize their own. Such altered behavior is called "habituation." Not all carrot cultures undergo this change, nor do we know the exact conditions necessary to bring it about, but that such a change does sometimes occur seems to be a fact whose elucidation should be of very great importance for our understanding of tissue growth in general.

Another tissue that has been very instructive is that of the tubers of the Jerusalem artichoke. Tissues of most plants, when first isolated, contain some residual auxin and will make a little growth on a simple nutrient, though the growth soon stops. But tissues taken from mature artichoke tuber tissues have no residual auxin and make no growth at all. They are therefore especially good material in which to study the precise effects of graded series of auxin concentrations. Tissues of kohlrabi, on the other hand, contain so much residual auxin that in test-tube cultures they poison themselves and cannot undergo cell division; the cells merely explode into enormous blisters.

Tissues of grapevines can be used as a medium on which to study the behavior of the downy mildew *Plasmopara viticola,* a parasitic plant that has not previously been amenable to study in the living condition in the laboratory. This approach will undoubtedly prove to be an important use of the tissue-culture technique. The same approach has permitted the study of tobacco mosaic virus and crown-gall infections in tobacco and tomato plants; the latter study has helped to clarify many points in regard to crown gall, as we shall see. Among other tissues that have been grown in cultures are those of hawthorn, rose, snapdragon, blackberry and Virginia creeper. One of the latest to be successfully established is willow. Though willow was one of the first plants studied, only after 15 years of intermittent investigation has Gautheret at last succeeded in deciphering the particular nutritional problem that this species presents.

The tissues of all these plants vary widely in their requirements and growth habits. Some, like the willow, require several vitamins and other substances; others, like the carrot, need only one, indole-acetic acid; still others, like the "habituated" carrot, are capable of growing without any external supply of vitamins or similar substances. Some possess a marked polarity of growth while others are without evident polarity. Some plants produce solid, firm cultures by a superficial proliferation over the entire surface. In others, proliferation is more deep-seated and in discrete areas, resulting in loose, friable, even powdery masses. Tissue cultures of the Virginia creeper are snowy white, those of the carrot yellow, those of *Scorzonera* almost black. The permutations of behavior patterns and of nutritional and other environmental requirements are almost endless, as are the potentialities for use and study of these cultures.

Here we come to an aspect of the investigation that was not envisioned at all in the beginning but has a particular cogency now. This is its application to the study of cancer. Tumors and cancers are parts of the body that have escaped from the social restraints characteristic of normal growth. In setting up tissue cultures we have deliberately removed those restraints. We have therefore transformed normal tissues into something possessing certain important resemblances to tumor tissues. These resemblances are artificial and we know how they have arisen. We can thus begin to understand some of the processes by which tumors may arise in nature. Moreover we now have a technique by which the tissues of plant tumors that occur in nature can be studied in the laboratory. Plants develop many different sorts of tumors, representing all the major types of cancers found in animals. They grow hereditary tumors, tumors caused by viruses, chemically induced tumors, tumors caused by organisms such as bacteria, and still others whose causes are not known. The tissues of all of these can be grown in culture. One of the facts learned by this means is that at least two groups of plant tumors are sterile, yet are capable of producing new tumors upon transplantation into healthy plants. Thus they possess qualities analogous to those responsible for the malignancy of cancer cells in man.

We have been able to learn a great deal about the steps involved in the production of some of these tumors. For example, tumor tissues, unlike normal ones, do not require externally applied auxins. If bits of normal tissue are placed beside bits of tumor tissue, the normal tissue will grow even on a nutrient lacking auxin. This suggests that the tumor tissue excretes auxin in quantities sufficient to permit the growth of the neighboring normal cells. Other experiments confirm this suspicion. Slices of chicory placed on moist sand will ordinarily form buds on the upper surface and roots on the lower, but the production of buds can be suppressed either by applying auxin paste to the upper surface or by grafting bits of tumor tissue into this surface. In other words, the tumor tissues can substitute for the auxin paste. Moreover, tumor tissues do not show the characteristic growth responses to moderate dosages of auxins that normal tissues show. All of these bits of evidence indicate that tumor tissues must produce auxins and that one of the changes a normal plant cell undergoes in becoming a cancer cell is an increase in its ability to manufacture auxins, or at least to make them available. We can study the way in which this change comes about.

One of the unexpected facts uncovered in these studies is the extreme rapidity with which the change from normal cell to tumor cell takes place. Armin C. Braun of the Rockefeller Institute for Medical Research has shown that in crown gall, a plant tumor started by bacteria, the transformation of normal cells into malignant ones is completed in 10 hours, within a critical temperature limited to a range of only three degrees. This is much more precise information than has ever been obtained about the origin of any animal tumor.

Several laboratories are investigating intensively the whole range of environmental factors involved in the satisfactory maintenance of cultures of both normal and tumorous plant tissues—nutrient ions, energy sources, specific organic nutrients, nutrilites, vitamins and hormones, temperature, light, acidity, osmotic values and so on. We already know a great deal more about the requirements of plant tissues and what can be accomplished by modifying their environment than we do about the corresponding requirements of animal tissues. In fact, the picture has changed so radically in the past decade that we are now trying to apply to animal tissue cultures some of the methods that have proved so fruitful in studying plants. We hope, for example, that these methods may help to unravel the almost hopeless nutritional tangle in which the classic technique of animal tissue culture, using a nutrient of embryo juice and blood plasma, finds itself.

The chief obstacle in the way of progress in this very promising field today is the lack of sufficient trained personnel to carry on. It is to be fervently hoped that this lack may be corrected in the next few years.

PART 4 GREEN LEAVES AND RED

I. PROGRESS IN PHOTOSYNTHESIS

by Eugene I. Rabinowitch

At Berlin, Göttingen, Copenhagen, London and M.I.T., Eugene I. Rabinowitch acquired a formidable background in physics and then biochemistry in preparation for his distinguished career as a botanist. His principal field of interest is the baffling problem of photosynthesis, and he is recognized as one of the world's leading authorities on the subject. *Photosynthesis*, by Rabinowitch, issued periodically in revised editions, is the definitive work. The challenging possibility of setting other chemical traps for solar energy has also attracted his energies; his thionine-iron cell is one of the most efficient yet devised. During the war, Rabinowitch was on the staff of the Manhattan District and came out of that experience as one of the most concerned and articulate "atomic scientists." With the late Hyman H. Goldsmith in 1946 he founded the *Bulletin of the Atomic Scientists,* which they issued first as a mimeographed emergency newsletter with a household circulation among scientists. It has functioned ever since as this country's central forum of opinion on the knotty controversies surrounding the domestication of nuclear technology. Today it goes to a circulation of more than 15,000 influential readers in and outside of science and all over the world. The *Bulletin's* back issues provide an unmatched record of the first decade of the age of the atom and are a tribute to Rabinowitch's prescience and energy as an editor. Born in St. Petersburg (Leningrad) in 1901, Rabinowitch came to the U.S. from England in 1939. He is now research professor in the department of botany at the University of Illinois.

II. AUTUMN COLORS

by Kenneth V. Thimann

Revered by his many students (several are contributors to this book) as one of the principal figures in modern botany, Kenneth V. Thimann is known to an entirely different group of contemporaries as a formidable innovator in modern naval warfare. He took war leave from his professorship at Harvard University to work with and head up operational research teams concerned with antisubmarine, convoying and carrier operations, and returned to botany with the title of Director of the Air Operations Research Group of the U.S. Navy. The son of a minister of the English Congregational Church, Thimann was also the younger brother of a chemist, who introduced him at an early age to the fascination of this branch of learning. At the Royal College of Science, London, his interests were further channeled into biochemistry by "a very good course in botany." Upon receiving his doctorate in 1930, he came to this country with an appointment as instructor in biochemistry at California Institute of Technology. Here he joined Herman Dolk in a preliminary investigation of the so-called plant-growth hormone, whose existence had been postulated at that time. Thimann was able to isolate such a substance and identify it with the known compound, indole-acetic acid. On the death of Herman Dolk in 1933, Frits Went came to Pasadena, and he and Thimann entered into a collaboration on a hormone governing the formation of roots, for which Went had assembled evidence in Java (it turned out to be identical with auxin). Together they wrote the first major text on auxins and their role in plant physiology. Thimann was called to Harvard in 1935 and has been there ever since.

PROGRESS IN PHOTOSYNTHESIS

by Eugene I. Rabinowitch

P HOTOSYNTHESIS—the synthesis of organic compounds from carbon dioxide and water by plants in light—remains one of the great unsolved problems of biology. If investigators of this process have made any progress in recent years it may be summed up in the conclusion that photosynthesis is much more complex than used to be thought. In spite of extensive work by many investigators, the task of separating it from other life processes in the cell and analyzing it into its essential chemical reactions has proved to be more difficult than was anticipated.

The photosynthetic process, like certain other groups of reactions in living cells, seems to be bound to the structure of the cell; it cannot be repeated outside that structure. We can imagine that several enzymes, concerned in the sequence of chemical transformations, are arranged in a structural frame, and the molecules undergoing transformation are hustled through this structure along prescribed paths, like palace visitors on a conducted tour. There is a special reason for such a mechanism in photosynthesis: the process produces unstable intermediates which cannot be permitted to tumble around freely in the reaction space lest they be lost by recombination. Before the products are permitted to leave the catalytic structure, they must be converted into molecular oxygen at one end and into organic compounds (such as sugars) at the other.

Much has been learned about the structure of the photosynthetic apparatus. Chlorophyll, the catalyst that is essential to photosynthesis, is located in almost all plants in the so-called chloroplasts, small green bodies within the cells. There it often appears to be concentrated in even smaller particles called grana. The electron microscope has shown that the grana are flat and cylindrical, about half a micron in diameter and about a fifth of a micron thick. A granum is sometimes seen to disintegrate into 20 to 30 thin disks, like an overturned pile of coins. It has been suggested (on the basis of treatment with different solvents) that these disks are made principally of proteins and are held together by a principally fatlike substance, like bread slices stuck together with layers of butter. Each disk is only a twentieth of a micron thick—the thickness of a single or double layer of protein molecules.

Some chloroplasts—in particular, those of the algae—contain no grana; instead, the whole chloroplast consists of thin, parallel, platelike structures, called lamellae. Improved electron micrography of grana-bearing chloroplasts shows that they, too, contain lamellae running through the whole body of the chloroplast. In such chloroplasts, the lamellae here and there thicken, forming denser structures seemingly disjoined from the main lamellae layers and arranged in the cylindrical "stack of coins" pattern identified with the grana. These denser regions appear as grana on electron micrographs of dried-out or disintegrated chloroplasts.

What light may these facts shed on the disposition of the chlorophyll and the plot of the photosynthetic play? It is known that the chlorophyll molecule has the shape of a tadpole with a green, square, flat head ("chlorophyllin") and a long, colorless tail ("phytol") attached to one corner of the head. In the social life of organic molecules, like attracts like. The head of the chlorophyll molecule is "polar," that is, it carries a positive and a negative charge. Water also is a polar compound. Since polar molecules associate with other polar molecules, the chlorophyllin head is attracted to water; it is "hydrophilic." On the other hand, the tail is nonpolar, therefore "hydrophobic." Proteins are hydrophilic and lipoids are hydrophobic. It has been surmised that chlorophyll accumulates at the boundary between the protein disks and the lipoid layers, with its head sticking into the protein and its tail dipping into the lipoid. This picture is speculative, but eminently plausible.

From analysis of leaves and algae, it is estimated that there are about one billion molecules of chlorophyll in an average chloroplast. Spread out in a monomolecular layer, a billion chlorophyll molecules, it can be calculated, would cover 1,000 square microns. Now the interesting thing is that if we multiply the area of a protein disk (.4 of a square micron) by the number of disks in a granum (about 25) and then multiply that by the number of grana in a chloroplast (about 100) we also get 1,000 square microns. In other words, there is just about enough space on the surface of the disks for the available chlorophyll to cover them with a monomolecular layer. The calculation claims no precision beyond that of the order of magnitude, but even so the agreement is gratifying.

It is a tempting hypothesis that the protein disks are the stage upon which the structure-bound part of photosynthesis is played. Some of the proteins in these disks may take the star roles of enzymes, while others may play supporting roles. The lipoid layers between the disks provide avenues for the diffusion of nonpolar organic intermediates to and away from the disks. Other reactions of photosynthesis, not structure bound, may be completed there, or perhaps even outside the grana or outside the chloroplast itself.

The nearest thing to photosynthesis yet achieved outside the living cell is the so-called "Hill reaction," named after the Cambridge University plant physiologist Robin Hill. He showed that chloroplasts that were separated from the cell and suspended in water could oxidize water in light, liberating oxygen. But they need an outside supply of oxidant to maintain this oxidation for any length of time. Various oxidants—ferric salts, ferricyanide, quinone, many organic dyes—have been found suitable for the purpose.

In photosynthesis the oxidation of water is effected by carbon dioxide. This requires considerable energy, because water clings tenaciously to its hydrogen atoms and carbon dioxide is extremely reluctant to take on hydrogen. The energy is supplied by light, which is then stored as chemical energy in the plant. The oxidants used in the Hill reaction accept hydrogen much more readily than carbon dioxide does; therefore the reaction does not store as much light energy as photosynthesis does.

Several investigators have tried to increase the storage of energy by supplying chloroplast suspensions with increasingly reluctant oxidants. These attempts run into the difficulty I have already mentioned: the instability of the intermediate products and their tendency to react back. It is like pitching a ball onto a roof. The ball will keep falling back unless it is trapped by a gutter. In the living cell some enzymes evidently function as traps, holding the intermediate products at the high level of energy to which they have been boosted by light. These enzymes are lost in the preparation of chloroplast suspensions. The problem is to find out what they are and how they act.

Severo Ochoa and Wolf Vishniac at New York University and L. J. Tolmach at the University of Chicago have contrived artificial traps. As oxidants they offered to chloroplasts pyridine nucleotides, which are only slightly less reluctant hydrogen acceptors than carbon dioxide. As the trap they used pyruvic acid, and they added certain enzymes to "funnel" hydrogen into the trap. It was hoped that the enzymes would get hold of some of the hydrogen atoms tossed upon the pyridine nucleotides and would transfer them to pyruvic acid before they rolled back. The products of reduction of pyruvic acid are relatively stable. Thus some of the intermediary oxidation products of water, lacking unstable partners with which to react back, might be converted into oxygen which would escape from the cell.

The trap worked. Some pyruvic acid was indeed reduced, and an equivalent amount of free oxygen was evolved into the atmosphere. But the oxygen yields so far have been very poor. Perhaps photosynthesis in the living cell owes its high efficiency at least partly to structural properties of the trapping agents, which are lost in the breakup of the cells. There are indications that only enzyme molecules attached to a piece of chlorophyll-bearing structure are effective in transforming the intermediates formed in that piece.

In 1948 a Russian physical chemist named A. A. Krasnovsky discovered a chemical reaction of chlorophyll in solution which may bear some relation to the way in which light-excited chlorophyll mediates the transfer of hydrogen atoms from water to carbon dioxide. He illuminated chlorophyll solutions in pyridine to which ascorbic acid (vitamin C) had been added. Ascorbic acid is a mild reductant. It was oxidized, and chlorophyll was reduced to a pink compound. When the light was turned off, the reaction went back. The reversal was especially rapid if an oxidant, such as air or quinone, was added. The net result was the oxidation of ascorbic acid and the reduction of the added oxidant, with chlorophyll having acted as a "photocatalyst," as in photosynthesis. Krasnovsky adduced some evidence that even a pyridine nucleotide can be reduced by chlorophyll solutions in this manner— which would be a very remarkable result, since, as we recall, chloroplasts reduce these compounds only if an elaborate trap for hydrogen atoms is provided.

Of course taking hydrogen atoms away from ascorbic acid is much easier than taking them away from water. Thus the "Krasnovsky reaction" bears the same relation to the "Hill reaction" as the latter to photosynthesis. The Hill reaction can operate on the same reductant (water) as photosynthesis, but it requires more willing oxidants than carbon dioxide. The Krasnovsky reaction can use the same oxidants as the Hill reaction (say quinone), but it requires a more willing reductant than water.

In 1937 Joseph Weiss and I found that chlorophyll in solution can be reversibly oxidized by ferric salt. The degree of oxidation is enhanced in light. Here, too, some light energy—although perhaps only a small amount—is stored as chemical energy. Chlorophyll is thus a very peculiar substance: it can act both as an oxidant and as a reductant! It may perform either of these functions, or both, in photosynthesis.

Further experiments are desirable on the photochemistry of chlorophyll preparations, including not only solutions but also colloidal or crystalline particles and monomolecular layers, imitating the hypothetical arrangement of chlorophyll molecules in the living cell.

The main chemical job of photosynthesis is to reduce carbon dioxide to carbohydrate, from which all organic matter on the earth is derived. We have dealt so far only with the take-up of light energy to liberate oxygen from water and to transfer hydrogen to various more or less unwilling acceptors. The hydrogen acceptor is the bridge that leads from photosynthesis the powerhouse to photosynthesis the chemical factory. In the opinion of many investigators, there is a "universal" hydrogen acceptor (always associated with chlorophyll in the grana) which, after taking up the hydrogen from water in light, transfers it without further help from light to whatever compound is to serve as the ultimate oxidant, be it carbon dioxide or quinone or pyridine nucleotide. It seems most likely that if this first product is not utilized immediately it is lost by back reactions within a matter of seconds, although some investigators believe that the cells retain their reducing power for several minutes after light is shut off.

The next question is: By what chemical mechanism does the primary reduction product convert carbon dioxide into a carbohydrate? Here the isotopic tracer method comes to our aid. By supplying cells with carbon dioxide tagged with radiocarbon, letting them use it for a few seconds and then killing them, Melvin Calvin, A. A. Benson and their co-workers at the University of California and Hans Gaffron, E. W. Fager and associates at the University of Chicago concluded that the first product incorporating CO_2 in photosynthesis is phosphoglyceric acid, a combination of phosphoric acid and glyceric acid; it seems to be as universally useful in metabolic processes as lubrication in machinery. Looking at the glyceric acid part only, we note that this compound, $C_3H_6O_4$, is halfway between CO_2 and glucose, $C_6H_{12}O_6$, in respect to the number of carbon atoms. It is more than halfway in respect to the "reduction level," i.e., the ratio of hydrogen to oxygen atoms in the molecule, which is zero in carbon dioxide, 1½ to 1 in glyceric acid and 2 to 1 in glucose. Thus glyceric acid is an appropriate halfway station on the path from carbon dioxide to sugar. Probably carbon dioxide is first grafted upon some organic compound present in the cell, and this product is then reduced in light to glyceric acid. Subsequent transformations of glyceric acid must lead to the formation of glucose and to regeneration of the carbon dioxide acceptor, permitting the repetition of the cycle.

This picture of a process in which the growth of the carbon chain and its reduction to the carbohydrate level are carried out with a carbon dioxide molecule grafted upon a carrier comes naturally to biochemists. They use similar mechanisms to explain respiration, the reverse of photosynthesis—i.e., in respiration organic molecules such as glucose are broken down and oxidized to water and carbon dioxide. The best known example of such a mechanism is the so-called Krebs cycle. Some of the reactions in this cycle are reversible: that is, they occur with little release of energy and could be made to run backward simply by supplying their products in overabundance and removing the synthesized organic compounds by some trapping mechanism.

The reduction of carbon dioxide in photosynthesis could conceivably proceed simply by reversal of the Krebs cycle, in which case the CO_2-acceptor could be pyruvic acid, a compound with a simpler formula ($C_3H_4O_3$) than glyceric acid. But the process is not that simple. Instead, more recent tracer experiments at Berkeley have suggested that the CO_2 molecule is accepted by a pentose diphosphate (pentose is a carbohydrate—a "sugar" with five carbon atoms in the molecule; the most common sugars—glucose, lactose, etc.—are "hexoses," with a six-membered carbon chain). By adding CO_2 to a pentose and binding water in the product we can produce two molecules of glyceric acid (we forget again about the phosphate part). The reaction goes like this: $CO_2 + C_5H_{10}O_5 + H_2O \rightarrow 2\ C_3H_6O_4$. Benson in Berkeley and Horecker at Bethesda, Maryland, have both proved independently that green cells contain an enzyme which catalyzes this reaction in the test tube.

The path of carbon in photosynthesis, traced by Calvin and co-workers on the basis of these data, starts with the formation of glyceric acid from pentose and CO_2. Then with the help of hydrogen from a light-produced reductant, the reaction proceeds with the removal of one oxygen atom from glyceric acid to form a triose, a sugar with only three carbon atoms ($C_3H_6O_3$), plus water. This reaction is written: $C_3H_6O_4 + 2H \rightarrow C_3H_6O_3 + H_2O$. The cycle ends with the transformation of the triose molecules partly into a hexose as final product and partly back into the pentose acceptor needed to take up more CO_2 and thus renew the cycle.

Recent experiments by Kandler (in Munich) have suggested an important correction of the Calvin road map of carbon-dioxide transformations. They indicate that glyceric acid may not lie on the main highway of photosynthesis at all, but that the corresponding true intermediate is the "double" molecule, $C_6H_{10}O_7$. This molecule can be hydrolyzed into two glyceric acid molecules. It is so hydrolyzed when the cells are killed by boiling alcohol, as they have been in Calvin's work. The reduction of $C_6H_{10}O_7$ by four hydrogen atoms from a light-activated hydrogen donor can lead directly to a hexose, $C_6H_{12}O_6$, and water is a by-product. Thence, the reaction can lead, in part, back to the pentose-CO_2-acceptor needed to start the cycle again.

This seems at present the most likely chemical mechanism of the conversion of CO_2 to hexose with the help of a light-activated hydrogen donor, derived from H_2O. It may not be the final, or the only, mechanism. In analogy with what we know about the multiplicity of respiration paths, it is by no means certain that photosynthesis takes the same one under all conditions and in all organisms. The upstream path of photosynthesis may branch and communicate on many levels with the descending paths of respiration. Through these cross-connections intermediate products of respiration may be fed into the pumps of photosynthesis and intermediates of photosynthesis may find their way back into the downstream of respiration.

AUTUMN COLORS
by Kenneth V. Thimann

For those of us who live in the Northeast the summer may be short-lived, but it expires in a blaze of glory, and all the trees put on fancy dress for its passing. From the soft old gold of the birches through the flaming scarlet of the rock maples to the rich crimson of the red oaks and sumacs, there is a wealth and variety of leaf color which compares very favorably with the flowers of our summer gardens. And the comparison is apt, for many of the pigments involved in autumn foliage colors are the same as those of the flowers.

The color changes involve both the fading or bleaching of the original pigments and the formation of new pigment types. The simplest case is represented by the yellow colors, which occur in the birches, poplars, elms and many other trees, as well as in almost every garden plant toward the end of its life span. The yellow pigments that make their first appearance in leaves in the autumn were present all the time, but were hidden from sight by the somewhat greater amount of green substances—the chlorophylls.

To appreciate these and other color changes one must consider what actually happens when an object appears colored. When white light, consisting of all wave lengths of the spectrum from about 400 to 710 millionths of a millimeter, falls on a surface that contains pigments, the pigments absorb some wave lengths more than others. Suppose that the pigments are such that the shortest wave lengths (those that would appear to the eye as violet) are the most absorbed, a little of the blue is absorbed, and our eyes see the remainder—a mixture of red, yellow, green and some blue. This mixture does not add up to white but to yellow. To put it in another way: white minus violet equals yellow.

Every pigment has its own absorption spectrum, which is usually represented as a curve on a chart showing the extent of absorption of light by the pigment at each wave length. The chart opposite shows the absorption spectra of a complete leaf (in this case a spinach leaf), and of some leaf pigments—a yellow pigment called carotene and the two kinds of green chlorophylls, called (rather unenterprisingly) a and b, that are present in most leaves. Since the chlorophylls absorb light strongly in the blue and the red, and hardly at all in the green, the eye looking at a leaf receives principally green light, with some yellow and a little blue and violet. The result is a general sensation of green. Now the yellow pigments of the leaf, as the absorption spectrum of carotene indicates, absorb only blue and violet light, which are largely absorbed anyway by the chlorophylls. Consequently the yellow pigments do not very markedly change the visible color of the leaf, and this is the reason their presence is unnoticed. The absorption spectrum of a complete leaf, as the chart shows, is more or less the sum of the absorptions of the individual pigments (with minor differences), and the unabsorbed light which reaches our eyes is almost wholly limited to the green.

In the autumn, however, the chlorophylls begin to bleach, and now the yellow pigments become visible. The reason for the bleaching is only partly understood; in general it is a consequence of the breakdown of the proteins in the leaf cells that accompanies the leaf's aging. Because the chlorophyll is attached to some of this protein, its own stability gives out too.

But the real magnificence of the fall colors depends on the reds. It is evident that here a new pigment enters the scene, for no red is present in the typical summer leaf; although many young leaves

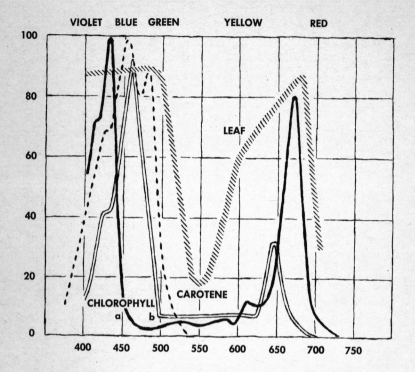

VIOLET   BLUE   GREEN   YELLOW   RED

Absorption spectra of the pigments in a leaf show why leaves turn
yellow. The chart shows percentage of light absorbed (*vertical
co-ordinate*) in each color or wave band of the spectrum (*horizontal co-ordinate*). Since the chlorophylls absorb red heavily, as
well as blue, they reflect green. The carotenes have much the
same blue absorption but they absorb little red and hence reflect
yellow and orange. When the chlorophylls bleach in the fall, the
carotenes become visible.

102

formed in the spring contain some red pigment, they lose it as they mature. Only a few leaves, such as those of the copper beech and some corn varieties, remain red throughout the season.

The red pigments newly formed in the autumn belong to a class of pigments quite different from those in the summer leaf. This class is best known to us in the form of the pigments of flowers. The very first flower pigment to be studied, extracted by the Frenchman F. S. Morot over 100 years ago, was not a red but a blue. He obtained it from blue cornflowers ("bachelors'-buttons"), and it was named anthocyanin, which means, in Greek, blue flower. (Chlorophyll, correspondingly, means green leaf.) The word anthocyanin is now used for a whole family of pigments, some blue, some purple and some red. A curious feature of these pigments is that their color in the flower is not always the same as that of the pure pigment; for example, the dark red rose has the same pigment (cyanin) as the blue cornflower. The reason for the difference in appearance is that other substances in the plant cells modify the chemical form, and therefore the color, of the anthocyanins.

Anthocyanins differ from the green and yellow pigments in at least two important ways. In the first place, they are fully soluble in water, whereas the chlorophylls, carotenes and related pigments are soluble only in oils or organic solvents. In the second place, as a result of their water-solubility the anthocyanins appear in the watery sap of the plant, while the green and yellow pigments are found only in the little green chloroplasts inside the leaf cells.

The study of how anthocyanins are formed, though very interesting, has not been pursued with any great vigor. The reason for this is to be sought in the curiously spotty nature of scientific progress. The advance of knowledge is like the advance of the tide over a level beach: in places it runs up long creek-beds to penetrate startlingly far inland, while at other points it creeps with extreme slowness up an incline or may even leave uncovered long spits of land stretching into the sea. Although mankind is entirely dependent on plant products, it remains true that very little effort has been expended on studying the processes by which these are formed. We may know something (though little enough) about the bulk materials, such as sugars, starches and proteins, but when it comes to the more subtle products of plants, e.g., drugs, dyes, vitamins and perfumes, our knowledge of the way in which they are formed is almost negligible. This is the more remarkable because the chemical structure of most of these has been thoroughly worked out, and even such a classical puzzle as the drug strychnine is now yielding up its long-guarded structural secrets to the organic chemists.

The anthocyanins have, like most plant compounds, been subjected to extensive study by organic chemists; their chemical structure has been cleared up and many of them have been synthesized. Yet we still have a long way to go to explain how they are formed in nature.

To study the mechanism of their formation the right biological material must be selected. Flowers and autumn leaves are too transient; the best material is something that can be cultured for a long period and that forms anthocyanin throughout its life. Some work has been done with red-colored seedlings such as buckwheat or red cabbage, some with leaves that form red pigment in summer (especially corn), and, most recently, some with duckweeds. These last are very convenient because they can be grown in sterile culture solution like bacteria. The peculiarities of the duckweed plant are described by Eric Ashby in his chapter, "Leaf Shape," page 73. In some members of the family, the little green leaflike fronds of the plant form purple pigment on the underside. It is the concentration of this pigment (which is of course an anthocyanin) that is measured. In our research on this material at Harvard University, the duckweeds are grown in a controlled medium in artificial-sunlight rooms, where the intensity of the light and the temperature can be accurately controlled.

The conditions under which anthocyanin is formed by the duckweed are most instructive for the understanding of fall colors. In the first place, light is required; the brighter the light, the more pigment. In the second place, the temperature must not be too high. Every New Englander knows that cool bright weather in the early fall favors the development of brilliant foliage, and here the experiments bear out the common observation. In England, on the other hand, where the autumn is usually rather mild and cloudy, autumn foliage color is duller, limited mainly to the yellows and browns; anthocyanins make a very minor, often undetectable, contribution. Consequently when the English poets write of autumn, they concentrate on the "mellow fruitfulness," the harvests and the Bacchic revels; autumn leaves for them are symbols only of decay. Shelley wrote:

> ". . . the leaves dead
> Are driven like ghosts from an enchanter fleeing,
> Yellow, and black, and pale, and hectic red,
> Pestilence-stricken multitudes."

The laboratory experiments also cast interesting light on the role of sugars in the formation of pigments. At the end of the last century experimenters observed that if various aquatic plants were floated on sugar solutions in daylight, they reddened. If duckweed is grown on sugar solutions it produces an increased amount of anthocyanin. Traces of anthocyanin can be formed from sugar even in the dark, but light very greatly increases the pigmentation. It follows from this that not only is light needed for the formation of sugar by photosynthesis, but there is actually a light-induced reaction of another kind which forms pigments. Both light and sugar are necessary.

Now, when sugar is oxidized or fermented in living cells, phosphate is always needed as well, for the sugar is broken down only after it has been combined with phosphate. When the influence of phosphate on anthocyanin formation was studied, it was found, surprisingly, that the depth of the pigment in duckweeds could be increased by cutting down the phosphate in the growth medium. With phosphate lowered to a few per cent of its normal value the pigmentation could be trebled. This is considered to support the idea that the pigment is formed through the accumulation of sugar by a process which takes sugar along a path quite different from that of its normal breakdown. The normal breakdown needs phosphate, but in the path leading to anthocyanin, phosphate apparently plays no part at all. Copper seems to play some role in this special path, for if a compound which combines strongly with the traces of copper that are present is added to the medium and the metal is thus denied to the plants, anthocyanin is not formed.

The effect of phosphate reminds one that scientific farmers have often observed that the leaves of crop plants become reddish or purplish as a characteristic response to a shortage of phosphate in the soil. It is one of the typical "hunger signs," and while such reddening may have several causes, phosphate deficiency is one of the commonest and the most important. The phosphate effect also recalls the fact, discovered by Raoul Combes at the Sorbonne many years ago, that many nutrients (of which phosphate is one) migrate out of the leaves into the stem as autumn comes on.

All of these observations and experiments add up to a general picture of a variant type of sugar metabolism which, with the aid of light, gives rise to the anthocyanins and perhaps also to other special products of the plant.

A complete explanation of autumn colors will have to involve at least four different factors: (1) the natural aging of the leaf, which causes phosphate and nitrogen compounds to go back into the stem; (2) the continued formation of sugars, provided the weather remains bright; (3) the presence of a specific chemical system or pathway, varying with the plant species, for the conversion of sugars into pigment, and (4) temperature. It may be that the low temperatures of autumn nights cause starch in the leaf to be converted to sugar and thus reinforce the second factor.

A full understanding of the pathway leading to the autumn color pigments might provide answers to much wider questions in organic chemistry and biology. The sugars, such as glucose, belong to a class of compounds called aliphatic; that is, they contain carbon atoms linked to each other in the ordinary way—a chain of six carbons, with the fifth carbon hooked back to the first through an oxygen atom and the sixth carbon at the side. The anthocyanins, however, belong to the class called aromatic, in which the carbon atoms are linked in the characteristic benzene ring of six, with electrons oscillating between them to give a taut and vibrating stability to the ring (see diagrams on next page). Oxygen atoms, when present, are linked to the side of the ring. A typical aromatic compound of this kind is phenol. Now the phenol arrangement occurs in all anthocyanins. The pigment of the duckweeds, and indeed of most red and purple leaves, is a compound of a phenol derivative, cyanidin, with certain sugars.

Just how aromatic compounds are formed in nature we do not know. The first products of photosynthesis, that great synthetic process which directly or indirectly supplies all the world's food, fuel, clothes, drugs, vitamins and so forth, are almost certainly aliphatic compounds—apparently sugars and the simple organic acids related to them. The aromatic compounds must therefore be produced by secondary reactions. If these reactions start from sugars, they involve a remolding of the aliphatic structure to join the six carbon atoms in a ring. Such remolding would represent a fundamental change that is virtually impossible to accom-

Molecular structures illustrate the problem of explaining how aromatics are formed. At upper left is the structure of the simple sugar glucose, one of the so-called aliphatics. Note the oxygen atom (O) at one of the corners of its central hexagon. At upper right is the structure of phenol, one of the aromatics. Here the oxygen atom has been replaced by carbon (C) to form the hexagon or the benzene "ring." At the bottom is the structure of the anthocyanin, cyanidin, which is found in the autumn leaf and which, as can be seen, contains the six-carbon rings of the aromatic family. The recasting of sugars into aromatic compounds is a feat not yet performed in the laboratory.

plish in the laboratory, but judging from the frequency with which aromatic compounds occur in nature, it must take place easily in plants. It is quite possible that it requires very extensive dismemberment and reassembly of the sugar molecules. In cyanidin the two six-carbon benzene rings are joined by a structure containing three carbon atoms. Since the breakdown of six-carbon sugars in nature involves splitting them into halves, each containing three carbon atoms, one may naturally suggest that the three-carbon bridging structure in cyanidin comes from a sugar. As yet this has not been proved. However, we find that anthocyanins and many other aromatic compounds very commonly occur in combination with sugars in the plant, which certainly suggests that they have a common origin.

The important aromatic compounds in nature include benzene itself, naphthalene, the lignin of wood, the photographer's developer quinol, some of the vitamins, a host of drugs (e.g., morphine, strychnine, quinine), most of the natural dyes, and of course the anthocyanins of flowers and autumn leaves. The parent substances from which all these are derived—benzene, phenol and naphthalene—are obtained chiefly from coal tar, a product of plants that died long ago. Upon these few naturally occurring compounds the vast structure of modern synthetic chemistry has been erected. It is not too much to say that benzene is a key substance for modern civilization. And it may be that the manner of formation of the anthocyanin pigments will provide a clue to the way in which nature produces benzene. Thus the study of autumn colors, like so many apparently minor problems in biology, leads us straight to the heart of the organism's activities, and a full explanation of the coloring, when we reach it, may yield explanations of many other biological mysteries.

PART 5 PLANT DYNAMICS

I. PLANT MOVEMENTS
by Victor A. Greulach

II. THE RISE OF WATER IN PLANTS
by Victor A. Greulach

Like so many other American scientists, Victor A. Greulach did his undergraduate work at a midwestern liberal arts college. At DePauw, in 1925, he first planned to major in English, but his interests were attracted to botany by Truman G. Yuncker, a teacher and investigator who has supplied graduate schools with "far more than his due share of students." At Ohio State University he took his doctorate in plant physiology, and went on to professorships in his field at the University of Houston and the A. & M. College of Texas. At the University of North Carolina he continued his work in plant physiology with emphasis on plant-growth substances and photoperiodism. Greulach is also a teacher with an ardent concern for the improvement of education in biology at the undergraduate and secondary school stages. He is the author of laboratory manuals and coauthor of a general textbook in botany soon to be published. His two contributions to the present volume reflect another active interest; he has written numerous articles for lay readership and worked with committees dedicated to improving the public communications of science.

PLANT MOVEMENTS

by Victor A. Greulach

Almost anyone asked to tell the differences between plants
and animals would mention that animals move while plants do
not. Even in the restricted sense of locomotion this is not quite
true. Some animals, such as corals, sponges and sea squirts, spend
their entire adult lives in a fixed position, while many plants are
able to move freely from place to place.

The slime molds slither about over old logs and stumps by
means of pseudopodia, much as an amoeba would. Many species
of diatoms swim under their own power; through a microscope
they can be seen gliding along in stately dignity like a ship in the
distance. They are believed to move by the streaming of protoplasm along a slit in the side, rather in the manner of a sidewheel
steamer. But most of the perambulating plants move themselves
by means of the long, whiplike structures known as flagella (or
cilia when the organism has a great number of them). The flagella-
using plants include some species of algae and bacteria, swimming spores of various algae and fungi and the swimming sperm
of plants, mostly the plant species without seeds.

Locomotion by flagella is more rapid than by protoplasmic
streaming. Some of the plant organisms using it reach a speed of
nearly three feet per hour. This may not seem fast to us, but in
relation to the size of these microscopic creatures it is stupendous.
A man running the 100-yard dash in 9.3 seconds travels about
seven times his height per second, and an F-68 Sabrejet at 650
miles per hour moves 25 times its length in a second. The zoospore of one fungus covers its own length as fast as a Sabrejet; the

flagellated bacterium *Pseudomonas aeruginosa* does a little better (31.7 lengths per second), and the zoospore of an *Actinoplanes* has been clocked at an amazing 99 lengths per second. To do as well in proportion to his size a man would have to be able to run at the rate of about 400 miles per hour!

In recent years, especially since the advent of the electron microscope, considerable attention has been devoted to the fine structure of flagella. All flagella studied so far, both from plants and animals, as well as the tails of animal sperm, apparently contain 11 strands arranged in the same way—two thin central strands and nine thicker outer ones. The rapid lashing of a flagellum seems to be due to the rhythmical contraction of these strands, usually first on one side and then on the other. These movements are produced by the contraction of proteins making up the strands—proteins like those in muscle.

My main purpose in this article, however, is to consider not locomotion but the less known and astonishingly various movements within plants. They are generally slow—as slow as a plant's growth—yet as dramatic in their way as locomotion, particularly when shown in time-lapse motion pictures.

The growth movements of a plant can be separated into three kinds: nutations, nasties and tropisms. Nutation is the spiral twisting of a stem as it grows. Generally it is most pronounced in vines. The stem tip first grows more rapidly on one side and then on the other. Apparently nutation (from the Latin word for "nodding") is controlled by some internal mechanism, not by external stimuli.

Nasties (or, more euphoniously, nastic movements) are among a plant's more beautiful motions: a typical example is the opening of a flower. They are the result of differing responses of different parts of the plant structure to the same external stimulus. When you bring a flower bud into a warm room, the rise in temperature causes the inner side of the petals to grow faster than the outer side, and the petals open. A drop in temperature sometimes reverses the process and closes the flower: e.g., in the crocus. The drooping of jewelweed leaves at night and their elevation during the day is a nastic response to light. Pigweed leaves are horizontal by day and more vertical by night. Oxalis flowers close at night and open during the day, while other flowers such as the evening primrose have the reverse response. Leaves can be made to bend downward by treatment with plant hormones or by exposure of the plant to ethylene or other similar gases. As little as one part of ethylene per 10 million parts of air makes tomato leaves bend down, so this plant can be used as an extremely sensitive test for gas leaks.

Of all the growth movements of plants, the most interesting are their tropisms—turning or bending in response to some outside stimulus. Everyone knows that a plant growing in a window bends toward the outdoor light. To explain this behavior by saying that the plant is seeking light is to credit the plant with a purposeful intelligence it does not possess. Actually the plant turns toward the light because the light reduces the concentration of growth hormone, or auxin, on the more brightly lighted side of the stem; as a result the darker side grows more rapidly and the stem bends. The light stimulus acts on the terminal bud where the auxin is produced, not on the stem itself. In the case of ivy growing on a wall, this tropism has a fascinating consequence: the shading of the leaf stalks by the leaves causes the stalks to bend in such directions that the leaf blades face the light with a minimum of overlapping, hence they are arranged in a mosaic.

Gravity is responsible for the tropism that makes a plant's stems and roots grow vertically. If a plant is placed in a horizontal position, the stems will bend upward near the tip and the roots will bend downward. Again auxin is responsible. When a stem lies horizontal, the auxin becomes more concentrated on the lower side. This causes the stem to turn upward, but it has the opposite effect on roots, because a concentration of auxin that promotes the growth of stem cells inhibits the growth of root cells.

Were it not for gravity tropism, called geotropism, agriculture would be impractical. Geotropism enables us to plant seeds any side up with confidence that the stems will come up. If plants grew only in the direction of the growing point on the seed, they might emerge from the ground at every conceivable angle, and the stems might even grow downward while the roots stuck up into the air.

Some plants, particularly twining vines and tendrils, have a tropism to contact. When a tendril touches a solid object, the cells on the side away from the contact suddenly elongate more rapidly, while those on the side of contact may shrink; so the tendril coils around the object. The response occurs within a minute or so, indicating that pressure effects as well as growth may be involved.

The general belief that plants have a tropism to water which makes their roots grow toward moist soil seems to be wrong. Recent research indicates that growth of roots by attraction toward water occurs only to a limited extent in a few species of plants, if at all. The reason that roots grow so thickly in moist soil, especially around drains, is simply that this environment favors the development of the rootlets already there.

We now come to movements produced by the swelling and shrinking of cells—called turgor movements. The agent here is water: diffusing into and out of cells, it inflates or deflates them, and it may raise the internal pressure in some plant cells to as high as several hundred pounds per square inch. Practically all leaves have pores which open when their guard cells are swollen with water and close when the guard cells are deflated, at night or when they lack sufficient water. The loss of pressure at night is connected with the halting of photosynthesis. When the morning light comes, the photosynthetic activity of the plant results in conversion of the insoluble starch in the guard cells into soluble phosphated sugar. The cells take up more water and swell.

A familiar example of turgor movement is the so-called "sleep movements" of plants of the legume, oxalis and similar families. At night, or when water is short, their leaflets fold together. The reason is that they lose the support of the cushion-like swellings at the base which ordinarily hold leaves and leaflets firmly erect. Another example is the rolling up of grass leaves in dry spells; they roll into a tube because certain rows of cells along their epidermis lose water more readily than others.

There are plants that exhibit much more rapid and spectacular turgor movements. The sensitive plant (*Mimosa pudica*), so called because it is sensitive to touch, shuts its leaves very rapidly when stimulated by a touch, by heat, by electricity or by ether. Sometimes you can see one pair of leaflets after another close in sequence as the impulse travels down the leaf.

In the barberry plant the lower parts of the pollen-bearing stamens are sensitive to touch. When an insect touches them, the stamens suddenly snap inward, dusting the insect with pollen. In the flowers of the trumpet creeper, catalpa and some other plants, a touch causes the two halves of the stigma to come together. If the stigma becomes covered with pollen during the process, the two halves remain together, but if no pollen was trapped, the halves separate within a few minutes.

Venus's-flytrap, an insect-eating plant native only along the Carolina coast, has a complex set of movements. Its leaves, hinged along the midrib, rapidly close together when their upper surface is touched. Usually it takes two separate touch stimuli, spaced 1.5 to 20 seconds apart, to make the leaf close; it shuts within half a second after the second touch. When it traps an insect or other

117

protein-containing object, the leaf remains closed and proceeds to squeeze its prey by pulling its edges together.

The aquatic bladderwort is another insect eater with rapid turgor movements. On its stem are many small sacs about the size of a pinhead. Each of these "bladders" is a trap, and it is set by being partly collapsed, like a squeezed rubber ball. It has a hinged trapdoor with a sensitive trigger. When a swimming insect or other small animal stimulates the trigger, the trapdoor suddenly swings upward and inward. A rush of water sweeps the animal into the bladder, and the door promptly closes. Inside, the insect dies and is digested. In the meantime, however, the trap is reset, and it may reopen to catch a second insect.

Still another insect-trapping plant is the sundew, which has small, sticky leaves with long tentaclelike hairs on the upper surface. When an insect becomes stuck on the leaf the hairs bend around it, and as soon as the tips of the hairs touch it the plant begins to secrete digestive enzymes. These hair movements are growth movements rather than turgor movements.

All these plant movements—locomotive, nutatory, nastic, tropistic, turgid and so on—are in addition to the usual restless traffic that goes on in any organism: the flow of water and food, the diffusion of substances in and out of cells, the multitude of biochemical reactions. The plant in the field, far from being a creature which toils not nor spins, is a veritable beehive of activity.

THE RISE OF WATER IN PLANTS
by Victor A. Greulach

THE giant redwood trees of California are very tall, but the Douglas firs of the Pacific Northwest are even taller; some of the firs have been known to reach a height of 400 feet. To reach the highest leaves of such a tree, water must rise from roots beneath the ground, a vertical distance of approximately 450 feet. How does the tree force its sap to this great height? Botanists have been puzzling over the problem for more than 200 years; even to-day we do not know the complete story of how water travels upward through plants.

Many wrong explanations have been proposed, and have enjoyed more or less wide acceptance. Yet as early as 1727 what we now believe to be the true account had been suggested. That was the year when Stephen Hales, a versatile English clergyman and scientist, published his *Vegetable Staticks*. In this historic work Hales laid the foundation for the science of plant physiology. A good portion of the book concerns his experiments on the rise of water in plants. Hales's methods and conclusions are surprisingly modern. Of the two mechanisms that are now thought to account for the phenomenon, he did considerable work on one, and at least hinted at the other.

What are the facts that a successful theory must explain? First, it must account for the origin of rather large forces. Merely to raise water 450 feet requires a pressure or tension of about 210 pounds per square inch. Friction between the water and the walls of the tubes which conduct it may call for almost as much force again, making the total 420 pounds per square inch.

119

Second, the theory must account for the speed of ascent and the volume of flow of water in plants. In some hardwood trees it rises at the rate of almost 150 feet per hour. A date-palm tree in a desert oasis may need to raise as much as 100 gallons of water a day to make up its losses from transpiration (evaporation, mostly from the leaves).

Finally, the explanation must fit the facts of plant anatomy and physiology. The upward flow of water in plants takes place in the xylem, or woody tissue. Throughout the xylem are many dead cells consisting only of cell walls and a central cavity. It is through these cavities that water passes. In trees of the pine family the water-conducting cells are called tracheids. They have spindle-shaped bodies as long as 3/16 inch and up to .0012 inch in diameter. In hardwood trees there are few tracheids; most of the water is carried through vessels that consist of chains of tubular cells whose end walls have dissolved away. These vessels may be more than three feet long and up to .015 inch in diameter.

The problem is to find the mechanism that forces the liquid up through these inert pipes. Probably most laymen, and even the authors of some biology textbooks, would answer that the water moves up by capillary action. Even in the thinnest tracheids, however, capillary rise could amount to no more than five feet, while in the larger vessels the limit would be two or three inches. Some students have pointed to minute tubes which exist in the walls of vessels and tracheids, claiming that capillary rise might take place in them. But we know that water moves through the cavities and not the walls, because plugging the cavities cuts off all flow.

There have been several so-called vital theories which hold that the living tissue in the xylem surrounding the vessels or tracheids acts in some way to force the water up. But plants whose stems, and even roots, have been killed may continue to absorb and conduct water for several days. The point was proved on a heroic

120

scale by a German botanist named Eduard Strasburger. He cut off a 70-foot oak tree close to the ground, immersed the end of the trunk in a vat of picric acid to kill its living cells, then dipped it in water and found that the water still moved to the top of the tree.

A more satisfactory explanation, in that it probably does account for the rise of water in some plants some of the time, is the root-pressure theory, originating in the work of Hales. He found that plant roots sometimes develop pressure due to their osmotic absorption of water from the soil, and suggested that this pressure accounted for the rise of liquid in the stem. Root pressure cannot, however, be the full answer, as Hales himself recognized. The greatest values of this pressure are far too small to raise water to the tops of tall trees; moreover some plants develop no root pressure at all. Finally, this mechanism could not elevate water nearly as fast as the sap sometimes rises in trees.

The only theory that seems to meet all the requirements was proposed in 1895 by H. H. Dixon, an Irish plant physiologist, and his co-worker J. Joly. It is variously called the cohesion theory, the transpiration stream, the transpiration-cohesion-tension theory and the Dixon theory. We shall add still another name—shoot tension—which is probably more accurately descriptive and which is comparable to the term root pressure.

The theory turns on an often-overlooked quality of water itself —its cohesion. If water is enclosed in a thin, air-tight tube, and does not contain too much dissolved gas, it has great tensile strength. Under the proper conditions such a column of water can withstand a pull of 5,000 pounds per square inch. Plant sap does not have quite as much cohesion as water, but its tensile strength has been measured at 3,000 pounds per square inch. Such a pull could theoretically lift a column of sap to a height of 6,500 feet, surely enough to account for the rise of sap in the tallest trees.

The sap, then, is capable of being pulled up. What pulls it? The force comes not from high pressure below, but low pressure above—the low diffusion pressure of water in the cells of leaves and other living parts of the shoot. As water is lost from the leaf cells by transpiration, or is used up in photosynthesis, digestion or growth, a water deficit is created in these cells. The resulting drop in their diffusion pressure causes the water to move inward from the liquid in the xylem by osmosis, and thus the entire water column, which is continuous from the leaves down to the roots, is pulled up. This in turn increases the difference in diffusion pressure between the root water in the tissues and the soil water, and water diffuses rapidly into the roots.

The tensions developed in the living cells of the shoot are more than adequate to pull water to the tops of even the tallest trees. Furthermore, the walls of the vessels and the tracheids have been found to be strong enough to prevent their collapse when the water in them is under tension, and they also appear to be sufficiently air-tight. The pressure differential between water in leaf cells and water in the soil is usually from 300 to 400 pounds per square inch, and may be even more. It is possible that the maximum shoot tension developed by trees of a particular species is an important factor in determining the maximum height to which these trees can grow. Shoot tension also accounts for the most rapid rate of water movement known in plants. In fact, the water is pulled up just as quickly as it is lost or used, provided the soil contains an adequate supply.

There are no basic theoretical objections to shoot tension as the mechanism of water-rise in plants, but it is rather difficult to understand how it can operate so efficiently. Why do the water columns not break as the tree sways in the wind? Why does cutting off a branch, even a large one, not disrupt the system? We

cannot yet answer such questions, but they do not seem serious
enough to undermine the theory.

In addition, we have considerable direct evidence that shoot
tension is actually operating in plants. If a vessel in a stem is laid
bare and punctured with a fine needle, the water column in it
snaps apart, as would be expected if the water were under tension instead of under pressure. H. F. Thut of Eastern Illinois
State College has demonstrated tension in another way. He attached tree branches to long glass tubes filled with air-free water
and immersed in containers of mercury (see diagram on page 125).
The tension created by the branches raised the mercury as high
as 40 inches, or about 10 inches higher than it could be forced by
the pressure of the atmosphere. This was equivalent to a water-
rise of about 46 feet. Still another experiment was performed by
D. T. MacDougal of the Carnegie Institution of Washington. He
reasoned that, if water ascends in trees by shoot tension, the
trunks should be slightly smaller in diameter during the day,
when the water is under greater tension and is moving most
rapidly, than at night. The inward pull on the walls of each vessel should add up to an appreciable decrease in diameter of the
trunk as a whole. MacDougal designed an extremely sensitive
device known as a dendrograph, which by a system of magnifying
levers could record minute changes in the diameter of the tree
trunks. He found that the trunks of trees are indeed somewhat
thinner during the day.

All this seems to add up to the fact that shoot tension accounts
for the ascent of water in most plants most of the time, although
root pressure apparently provides the motive force in some plants
some of the time. Now let us turn back some 200 years to Hales
and his *Vegetable Staticks*. After extensive accounts of his care-

ful experiments on root pressure he concludes: "These last experiments all show, that although the capillary sap-vessels imbibe moisture plentifully; yet they have little power to protrude it farther, without the assistance of the perspiring leaves, which do greatly promote its progress." Hales can be excused for believing that perspiration (transpiration) is required, for even today botanists assume that it is a component of the shoot-tension mechanism. Actually any use of water will provide the necessary water deficit.

Shoot tension is proved by joining a cedar twig to a tube filled with water *(top)* and mercury *(bottom)*. Atmospheric pressure will hold the mercury at 76 centimeters; the twig will lift it to 101.8 centimeters.

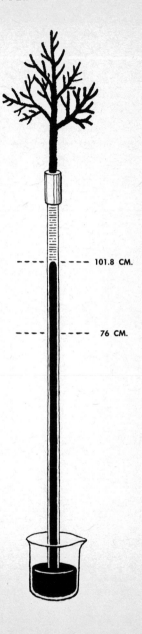

101.8 CM.

76 CM.

PART 6 EVOLUTION AND THE PLANT COMMUNITY

I. STRANGLER TREES

by Theodosius Dobzhansky and João Murça-Pires

The two authors bring quite different backgrounds to their collaboration on these strange plants. Theodosius Dobzhansky, professor of zoology at Columbia University, has spent much of his career unraveling the genetics of fruit flies. Murça-Pires, a Brazilian botanist, is an expert on Amazonian flora. Dobzhansky was born and educated in Russia. He "got excited" about biology at the age of ten, and dates his decision to specialize in genetics and evolution from his reading of *Origin of Species* when he was fifteen. After teaching at the University of Leningrad for a number of years, he came to the United States in 1927 as a Rockefeller Foundation research fellow to study with Thomas Hunt Morgan. At the end of his fellowship Morgan invited him to stay permanently. Biology in America has been enriched in consequence, not only by Dobzhansky's own significant researches but by the many fruitful careers his teaching has inspired. Murça-Pires is head of the botany division of the Instituto Agronomico do Norte in Brazil.

II. THE PLANTS OF KRAKATOA

by Frits W. Went

III. THE ECOLOGY OF DESERT PLANTS

by Frits W. Went

On one of his first assignments as a newly minted Ph.D., Frits W. Went worked at the Botanical Gardens in Java for a five-year period. During that time he had opportunity to make first-hand observations of the plant life on Krakatoa. At California Institute of Technology, one of the hazards faced by an under-graduate is an invitation from Professor Went to join him on one of his nonstop, dawn-to-dusk surveys of the plant life in the nearby desert; his account of the subject here reflects not only his intimate acquaintance with the desert but the useful-ness of his "phytotron," described in his chapter on "Climate and Agriculture," beginning on page 45.

IV. CHEMICAL SOCIOLOGY AMONG THE PLANTS
by James Bonner

Along with his six siblings James Bonner was set on a career in science at an early age by his father's "experimental outlook on things in general and his taking his children one by one into the laboratory and teaching us how to do experiments." He took his bachelor's degree at the University of Utah, where his father was professor of chemistry, and went on to California Institute of Technology for his doctoral training in 1934. There he was attracted into biology by a course taught by Theodosius Dobzhansky and into biochemistry and plant physiology by his work with Kenneth V. Thimann and Frits W. Went. Away from his laboratory at Cal Tech, Bonner is an active mountaineer and winter-weekend ski patrolman.

V. THE FERTILIZATION OF FLOWERS
by Verne Grant

When Verne Grant came upon the works of Charles Darwin in his early youth he then and there decided to become an evolu-tionary biologist. His interests were not much advanced in his Depression-years struggle for a bachelor's degree at the Uni-versity of California, because the Darwinian tradition was then at a low ebb in American universities. So upon graduation he heeded Darwin's advice, that "nothing can be more improving to a young naturalist than a journey in distant countries," and set out for the American tropics and later the high Andes where he spent several years as a free-lance naturalist. After the war he went back to Berkeley, resuming his studies under G. L. Steb-bins, who introduced him to the new science of evolutionary genetics via *Genetics and the Origin of Species* by Theodosius Dobzhansky and his own monumental *Variation and Evolution in Plants,* then in preparation. Grant's contribution to the present volume bespeaks his interest in the biology of reproduction and the modes of evolution in higher plants, the central theme of his work during the past ten years. He is chief geneticist at Rancho Ana Botanic Gardens at Claremont, California.

STRANGLER TREES

by Theodosius Dobzhansky and João Murça-Pires

PERHAPS the most troublesome problem in the theory of evolution today is the question of how the haphazard process of chance mutation and natural selection could have produced some of the wonderfully complicated adaptations in nature. Consider, for instance, the structure of the human eye—a most intricate system composed of a great number of exquisitely adjusted and co-ordinated parts. Could such a system have arisen merely by the gradual accumulation of hundreds or thousands of lucky, independent mutations?

Some people believe that this is too much to ask natural selection to accomplish, and they have offered other explanations. One school of thought suggests that evolution is directed not by natural selection but by some inner urge of organisms—an inscrutable something called "psychoid." Another theorist proposes that the marvelous gifts of evolution to the living world came to birth through sudden and drastic "systemic mutations," which created "hopeful monsters" that were later polished down to the final product by evolutionary selection. But these theories amount only to giving more or less fancy names to imaginary phenomena: no one has ever observed the occurrence of a "systemic mutation," for instance.

Actually we do not need to meander so far from the Darwinian theory. There is no necessity for assuming that the human eye, for example, had a sudden birth or that cruder forerunners of it could not have been useful to their possessors before the eye acquired its final perfection. The ancestors of the human species had eyes to see with, though they may have been less elaborate than ours. In short, the eye could have developed gradually from a very simple organ which in its earliest form gave some kind of "sight" or other useful ability to the animal that possessed it.

We shall consider in this article a most remarkable adaptation in the vegetable world which illustrates such a step-by-step evolution. In some exuberant rain forests of the tropics there grows a strange variety of plant known as strangler trees. Such a plant starts by seeding itself and growing like a vine on the trunk or branches of an ordinary forest tree. Climbing over its host, the strangler enfolds it in a thick mass of roots, strangles it to death and finally stands on its own as an independent tree!

The reason for the origin of the strangler trees (of which there are a number of species) is plain. In the dense tropical forest the competition for sunlight is keen. A young plant sprouting on the dark forest floor has a poor chance of survival unless it can somehow break through the canopy overhead. The stranglers have solved the problem by climbing on other trees. And the whole life history of these outlandish trees seems beautifully contrived to accomplish their objective: to seize a place in the sun in the midst of a dense tropical forest. How could this singular adaptation have arisen? Here is an extraordinary example of just the kind of complex adjustment that seems to justify some esoteric explanation such as "psychoids" or "systemic mutations." Let us see, however, whether a simpler explanation may suffice.

We need to consider first the life history of a strangler tree. Among the most common stranglers are certain fig trees (genus *Ficus*) of Brazil. The seeds of the strangler fig usually sprout high on the branches of a tall tree; just how they get there is not known, but there are reasons to believe that they may be carried by birds and fruit-eating bats. The young seedling produces roots of two kinds. One kind grows around the branch or the trunk of the supporting tree; the other descends toward the forest floor, either along the trunk or hanging in the air. The stem of the strangler sprouts leaves and grows upward to catch the sunlight. The young plant gets its water and its mineral food from accumulations of dirt and organic matter in crevices of the tree's bark. At this stage the future strangler is not a parasite, for it derives no nourishment from the living tissues of its host. It is an epiphyte, i.e., a plant which grows on another plant.

As soon as the descending roots take hold in the soil of the jungle floor, the growth of the strangler quickens. Its roots rapidly thicken and harden, and they put out many new branches and leaves. It is often difficult to tell from the forest floor which foliage belongs to the strangler and which to the host tree. New roots are formed, and they begin to branch on the surface of the supporting trunk. Eventually they form a mesh which envelops the host tree with an ever-hardening strangle hold. The appearance of a gigantic forest tree caught in the deadly embrace of a strangler is weird in the extreme. It makes one think of some of the grotesque creations of surrealist art, but it has the nobility and the purposefulness of life.

Now the strangler proceeds to kill the supporting tree. It does so not merely by preventing the trunk from expanding but actually by squeezing the tree. This is indicated by the fact that the strangler fig often kills palm trees, whose trunks grow steadily in length but little or not at all in thickness.

While the fig is throttling its host, its roots go on growing and hardening, until they completely or almost completely cover the trunk. They also form buttresses which enable the fig to stand on its own feet. By the time the supporting tree dies, the strangler has become an independent tree, with its own crown of branches

133

and leaves. Many specimens of these figs reach colossal dimensions, rivaling in height and girth some of the giants of the tropical forest.

At the final stage of its development the strangler may or may not show outward signs of its murderous past. Its "trunk," which in reality is a mass of fused roots, often has a bizarre shape, owing to the many cablelike or planklike buttresses. But it may also attain an almost regular cylindrical shape. In either case its true nature is readily exposed if one cuts through the mass of roots: inside there is a cavity which contains the more or less decomposed remains of the victim. Near Belém at the mouth of the Amazon stands a gigantic fig tree which has grown on the tall chimney of a brick factory abandoned some 70 years ago. The chimney is now all but invisible.

The Brazilian figs, which belong to the mulberry family, are one of many kinds of stranglers. Strangling trees are common not only in Brazil but also in rain forests of Australia, New Zealand and other places. But now, from the point of view of how the strangler trees evolved, we note a highly significant fact. There are many stranglerlike plants which do not strangle their hosts. A notable example is the Brazilian tree called *Clusia*. Some species of this genus behave like the strangler figs in every respect except one: they seldom if ever kill their support. We have seen thousands of jungle trees attacked by Clusia, and all of them were alive. High up in the forest canopy the large, leathery, dark-green leaves and the showy, rose-colored flowers of Clusia mingle with the foliage of the host tree. Adolfo Ducke, the leading authority on Amazonian flora, has informed us that he cannot remember having seen a Clusia that caused the death of its host tree.

Clusia may, then, illustrate an important stage in the evolution of the strangling habit. It is well adapted to use other tree species for support, and it is able to cling quite firmly to its host. But it stops short of killing the host tree and taking its place. When the host tree dies, Clusia presumably perishes with it, although further observations on this point are needed.

Still earlier stages in the evolution of the strangling habit may be seen in Brazil in three genera of plants of the mulberry family, to which the figs also belong. These genera are *Coussapoa*, *Pouroma* and *Cecropia*. Unlike the strangler figs or even Clusia, they may start in the soil on the forest floor and grow for their entire lifetime without climbing on other trees; they often grow in this independent fashion in forest clearings. The three genera show varying degrees of epiphytism: Coussapoa acts as a strangler frequently, Pouroma less often and Cecropia only occasionally.

It is remarkable that the strangling adaptation has evolved independently in several quite unrelated families of plants. The forests of New Zealand have no strangler figs or other stranglers of the mulberry family, but there is a strangler there called "rata" which is a member of the myrtle family. A rata kills and replaces its supporting tree in just the same way as a strangling fig. Yet a species closely related to rata grows on trees like a vine without strangling them.

E. J. Godley and L. J. Dumbleton of New Zealand have called our attention to still other plants in New Zealand forests which furnish striking illustrations of the probable stages of the evolution of the strangling habit. These plants belong to several different families: *Weinmannia* of the family *Cunoniaceae*, *Schefflera* of the *Araliaceae*, *Melicitus* of the *Violaceae* and *Griselinia* of the *Cornaceae*. Yet these rather remotely related plants are all capable of growing either as stranglers or as independent trees from the soil. It is not difficult to see how their versatility has evolved. The trees that they victimize most often are tree ferns—whose beautiful feathery fronds are so characteristic of the New Zealand forests. The trunks of the tree ferns are covered with a spongy mass of fibers, which in the rainy climate of many parts of New Zealand provides an inviting medium for seeds. Various species of plants have seized the opportunity and evolved adaptations which permit them to grow on such trees. After a time the evolving climber may lose the ability to start its life without the support of another tree; it is no longer a facultative strangler but an obligatory strangler. On the other hand, some members of the same plant genus or family keep their ability to grow independently.

Evidences of such evolution can be seen not only in New Zealand but also in the forests of Brazil. Some of the fig species there grow into huge trees without ever resorting to the strangling techniques of their relatives.

To summarize, a comparative study of the strangler trees shows that these amazing representatives of the plant kingdom possess quite a variety of adaptations for life under the exacting conditions of the tropical forest. The origin of these adaptations can easily be visualized as being due to nature's selection of useful hereditary modifications. This view is in accord with the modern theory of evolution, which considers selective responses of the organism to opportunities in the environment to be the primary driving force of the evolutionary process.

THE PLANTS OF KRAKATOA

by Frits W. Went

At two minutes past 10 on the morning of August 27, 1883, one of the most violent explosions ever experienced by man occurred on an island between Java and Sumatra in the East Indies. Although the nearest inhabited place was at least 25 miles distant, 36,417 persons in the region were killed, mainly by drowning in the tidal wave that followed the explosion. The blast was heard more than 1,000 miles away.

The source of this awesome detonation was the blowing up of the central part of Krakatoa, a volcanic island which had had a long history of disquietude. The island had begun to disintegrate several hours before the main explosion, and a series of pulverizing eruptions continued throughout the day. When men first dared to approach the island two months later, a sea 800 feet deep covered the major part of the island, where the volcanoes Perbuatan and Danan had once stood. Approximately six cubic miles of rock and pumice had been blown into the air! (Considering what can be done with thermonuclear bombs, it seems that these come close to the violence of such a volcanic eruption as that of Krakatoa.)

All that was left of Krakatoa was a ragged, 2,500-foot peak. It was completely covered with a thick layer of smoking pumice and ashes, still too hot to walk on with bare feet. Clouds of steam rose from many parts of the island, especially from the gullies that rain water had scoured in the loose pumice. All animal life, of course, had been wiped out. Not a tree, shrub or other plant survived.

A place so utterly desolate and devoid of life would hardly seem a promising site for an investigation of how plants and animals become distributed over the earth. When one gives the matter a little thought, however, he can see that such a sterilized island offers a marvelous opportunity for just such a study. To resettle sterile Krakatoa Island, all seeds, spores and animals had to cross a 25-mile stretch of sea. There was an island closer than this, Sebesi, about 12 miles north of Krakatoa, but most life on Sebesi had been destroyed by toxic gases and a thick layer of ash, and it was hardly a source of seeds or spores.

In May, 1884, nine months after the eruption, the French botanist E. Cotteau visited Krakatoa. He reported: "In spite of all my investigations, I was unable to observe any trace of animal or plant life with the exception of a single spider; this hardy pioneer of resettlement was busy spinning its web."

Three years after the eruption, a party led by the Dutch botanist Melchior Treub found a very different situation. On the beach were growing many of the plants commonly found along tropical seashores. Farther inland Treub found many ferns and some grasses, but very few other plants.

Unfortunately it was another 10 years before the island was revisited by botanists. By then it was fairly well covered with green: here and there stood groves of Casuarina (the horsetail tree), and there was a wide scattering of wild sugar cane. Four species of soil-inhabiting orchids were found. On the shores grew young coconut trees. In general, vegetation was much more abundant on the shores than in the interior.

It was not until 1906 that the island was densely covered with plants. The vegetation was then mostly grass with some trees here and there. By 1920 trees had taken over perhaps half of the surface, and in 1930 the whole island was again covered with a dense, though low and young, forest.

What does all this mean in explaining the natural distribution of plants over the world?

Since the vegetation of Krakatoa had been so completely destroyed, new plants could develop only from seeds and spores that were somehow transported to the island from other places. How might they have been carried?

In the first place there is the wind. Very light spores or seeds can be carried by even gentle air currents. Bacteria, for instance, are floating everywhere in the air, even in a perfectly quiet room. Spores of ferns are no heavier than pollen grains, which are commonly moved by a breeze from pine tree to pine tree to cause pollination. It is significant that almost half of the plants observed on Krakatoa three years after the eruption were ferns, whereas ordinary ferns constitute no more than 10 to 20 per cent of a stable tropical vegetation. The ferns' mode of distribution by means of very light spores gave them an advantage over most other plants. In later years plants with heavier seeds caught up, but in the beginning the ferns were the most numerous settlers.

Orchid seeds are almost as light as fern spores: there are many millions of them in an ounce. Most orchids require trees to grow on, or at least rich humus in the soil; yet in spite of the handicap of poor soil and treelessness on Krakatoa, 13 years after the eruption four species of orchid were flowering there, which shows that great numbers of orchid seeds must have been blown to the island.

Even heavier seeds can be carried by wind, especially when they are provided with hairs, such as those of cotton, cottonwood and dandelions, or with wings, as in elm fruits. Some of the first grasses found after the eruption undoubtedly also arrived on the wings of the wind. It is estimated that about 40 per cent of all species of plants now living on Krakatoa arrived there by this means. Thus the wind must be considered the most effective and important agent in dispersal of these tropical plants.

The seeds of certain other plants on Krakatoa, such as the coconut palm found flowering on its shores in 1896, are too heavy to be carried by wind. The big coconuts from which these trees sprang must have been brought by the sea. Coconut palms grow along the shores of all tropical islands in the Pacific and Indian Oceans. Under natural conditions they do not extend far inland. When the coconuts drop off, many get washed away by the sea. They remain afloat, and near tropical shores one can occasionally see a coconut bobbing up and down on the waves among logs and other flotsam. The fruits and seeds of most other tropical shore plants are similarly carried by sea currents over long distances. Experiments have shown that floating for several weeks in sea water does not injure them. They will germinate as soon as they are washed ashore and watered by rain water. A hard seed coat or a protective cover of strong fibers protects the seeds from injury when they scrape over the sand.

This natural experiment on Krakatoa explains why the coastal vegetation of all the Pacific islands is so uniform. The several dozen varieties of plants found on their shores have been distributed from island to island by the ocean currents. This method of distribution of seeds is so effective that even newly formed islands with no other flora are soon colonized by beach plants. Indeed, ocean transportation explains a striking phenomenon of the distribution of plants on great continents. Ordinarily we think of plants as spreading over land and being halted by oceans. But in Africa the beach flora of the continent's west coast is very different from that of the east coast. The former is like that of the east coast of South America, thousands of miles away across the South Atlantic, while the latter is like that of the islands of the Indian Ocean and the Pacific. The explanation is that the beach plants do not spread inland across the continent; they can travel only across the sea. Thus the varieties of shore vegetation, unlike most other plants, range around ocean basins instead of within continents.

In 1886 only plants distributed by wind and sea currents were found on Krakatoa. By 1896, however, some 9 per cent of Krakatoa's vegetation had arrived by other means, and today about 40 per cent of all its species have done so. In most of these cases it is very likely that the seeds were distributed by animals, usually by birds but occasionally by man.

In 1916 several men settled on Krakatoa to exploit the pumice. They brought with them certain fruit trees, such as mangoes. These survived only a few years. After the settlers had left, they were engulfed and obliterated by the dense jungle. Evidently our cultivated plants can survive only if helped by man in their struggle for existence. We know by experience how seldom a corn or tomato plant that escapes cultivation becomes established among the wild vegetation.

The majority of plants distributed by animals must have been brought to Krakatoa by birds. The occurrence of so many plants with fairly large seeds that could not have arrived by wind or water, and the fact that most of these plants have fleshy fruits that are eaten by birds, makes this almost a certainty. The seeds of many fruits which birds eat are not destroyed in their digestive tract, but are still intact and viable in their droppings. Thus any seeds remaining in the digestive tract of a bird that had flown across the 25 miles of sea between Java and Krakatoa would have a chance of germinating in its droppings. Among the plants presumably transported to Krakatoa by birds belong figs and papayas.

One might object that mistletoes, which are spread exclusively by birds, do not occur on Krakatoa as yet, though they are very abundant on the nearby islands. Observations have shown, however, that mistletoe seeds are spread almost exclusively by species of Dicaeum birds. These birds retain the seeds for no more than 12 to 20 minutes after ingestion, and therefore could not have carried them over a distance of 25 miles, which would require at least an hour's flight. Other birds, such as the tjalak, which is common in Java, can retain seeds in their intestines for at least 100 minutes; they do not eat mistletoe fruits, however, and therefore could only have transported other plants.

It is certain that birds can carry seeds for fairly long distances, but in the absence of evidence of any method of transport except in the food they have eaten, such dispersal is definitely limited by the length of time the birds hold their bowel contents. Charles Darwin believed, and in one case actually proved, that seeds could be distributed by sticking to mud on the legs of wading birds. This would explain the long-distance transportation of marsh plants, but there are no marshes on Krakatoa. It is of course possible that seeds may become attached to birds by some other means, but that is very hypothetical.

Another mechanism often invoked to explain the spread of plants is the attachment of seeds to floating logs, which may drift for great distances in sea currents. This is a very unsatisfactory hypothesis, because most seeds cannot stand contact with sea water. Besides, only a certain few plants can germinate and grow on beaches, as far inland as floating logs are washed. Yet this mechanism should not be entirely discarded. For example, I found two lizard eggs, which seemed viable, hidden in a cavity of a floating log that had been washed ashore on Krakatoa.

No matter whether we can agree in each case on how a certain plant reached Krakatoa, the important fact remains that all these plants arrived there by one means or another—this is the most significant result of the large-scale natural experiment initiated by the volcanic explosions on the island. One might assume, of course, that seeds of most of the plants later found there had survived August 27, 1883. One botanist has taken this stand, and has written a whole book to prove his contention. However, he has failed to convince other botanists that plants, seeds, roots or rhizomes were able to withstand fires, toxic gases and terrific explosions, and later a cover of hot ashes and pumice 20 to 200 feet deep that charred everything it touched. Two months after the eruption the whole island still steamed after a rain, indicating that temperatures near the boiling point still existed deep in the pumice.

The biology of Krakatoa is full of interesting problems. No stability has yet developed in its plant or animal life. For instance, some years the island may be overrun by rats, yet a year or two later the natural equilibrium will swing back to the point where hardly a rat can be found. Here is a typical example of a biological problem which was highlighted by the Krakatoa experiment: In the Asiatic tropics are many so-called ant plants in which ants have a permanent abode. The curious fact is that each kind of ant plant has its own kind of ant. Thus an epiphytic fern, *Polypodium sinuosum*, grows in Java on the branches of trees, and in its hollow rhizomes nests an ant called *Iridomyrmex myrmecodiae*. By one of the chances of distribution, this ant arrived on Krakatoa by itself before the fern had settled there. According to the biologist who first found the ants, they were running around nervously, obviously lost. When I visited Krakatoa several years later, I found the fern growing on branches of trees—and *Iridomyrmex* had settled in its rhizomes. The fern could only have been distributed in its spore form by the wind, otherwise it could not have started to grow on tree branches. The ant *Iridomyrmex* had lived on Krakatoa, alone and obviously unhappy, for many generations; the moment its symbiotic partner arrived, the old symbiosis, so rudely interrupted by the chances of dispersal, was re-established. This certainly is a most interesting example of instinct and the tenacity of characters of adaptation.

Krakatoa is, of course, a limited experiment. In evolutionary botany we want to explain the distribution of plants over much greater distances, not 25 miles as at Krakatoa, but 250 miles, 2,500 or even farther. If Krakatoa, however, had been located at such a distance from the nearest vegetation, it would have taken too long for seeds to arrive there; it might have been thousands of years before an appreciable number of plants settled and made a new vegetation cover.

Under most natural conditions, we actually have to count in millions of years when explaining the distribution of plants. Let us take another example from Java and Sumatra. Although these islands are fairly old in a geological sense, they did not have any high mountains until volcanoes developed on them. These volcanoes are of quite recent origin, not more than a few million years old. They reach up to almost alpine altitudes, and none of the typical lowland tropical plants can grow on their tops. On the other hand, most of the kinds of plants growing on their tops cannot possibly grow in the steaming lowlands. At high altitudes on these volcanoes we find buttercups, gentians, brambles and blueberries, which are never found at sea level in the tropics. They must have spread from volcano to volcano, and they must have done this during the last million years or so. Many of these volcano-hopping plants have edible fruits, and thus have a good chance to be spread by birds. But not all the volcanoes have all the plants growing on them that their climate and soil will allow. This shows that a million years is not quite long enough for chance to distribute seeds thoroughly over distances of up to 1,000 miles. Another case in point is the plant *Primula prolifera*, which originated in the Himalayas. It is now found on a few volcanoes in Sumatra—a distance of about 1,500 miles from its place of origin. In Java, 500 to 1,000 miles farther on, this plant is found on only three volcanoes, although about 20 are high enough for it to grow on. We see here that *Primula* has not only hopped from volcano to volcano, but has skipped them as well.

There have been other terrific volcanic eruptions, which sterilized hundreds of square miles. The explosion in Alaska in 1912 of

Mount Katmai, which disappeared and left only the "Valley of Ten Thousand Smokes," annihilated the vegetation over a wide radius. Katmai was on the mainland, however, and vegetation was able to infiltrate the sterilized area slowly from undamaged areas farther away. Thus not much could be concluded from it about the mode of distribution of plants. The Krakatoa experiment still stands as the most instructive in history.

THE ECOLOGY OF DESERT PLANTS

by Frits W. Went

The LAWS of human behavior are very much in dispute, largely because there are no obvious experimental approaches to them. But animal and plant behavior can be studied both in nature and in the laboratory, and the science of their ecology should eventually be helpful in the understanding of human relationships, for the basic laws which govern the interrelations among organisms in general must also underlie human behavior. Ecology is an extremely complex study. For a relatively uncomplicated case, from which we may be able to extract some generalizations about behavior, I want to take you with me to the desert to survey its plant life.

The desert is an ideal area for research. It is usually unspoiled by the encroachment of civilization. Its plant life is sparse enough to be studied conveniently in detail, and it shows clearly and primitively the effects of the physical factors at play in the environment. Most important of all, the desert climate is violent: winds sweep over it unchecked, and its temperature and rainfall swing between wide extremes. Rainfall may vary fivefold from year to year. There are so few rainstorms that the effects of individual rains can be measured. The desert's sharply contrasting conditions can be reproduced in the laboratory for convenient experimental investigation of the germination and growth of plants. And the desert has an unending lure for the botanist; in the spring it is a delightful place.

The most extreme desert in the United States is Death Valley. Screened off from the nearest source of water vapor—the Pacific

Ocean—by the tall Sierra Nevada, the valley bottom has an average annual rainfall of only 1.35 inches. It has almost no surface water —only a few springs bringing up the scanty runoff from the dry surrounding mountains. Since it is sunk below sea level, Death Valley has no drainage. As a basin which holds and collects all the material that may be washed into it from the mountain canyons, it has accumulated salts in its central part. Seen from above, this salt bed glistens like a lake, but a traveler on foot finds it a dry, rough surface, studded by sharp salt pinnacles which crackle and tinkle as they expand or contract in the heat of the day and the cold of the night.

In the salt plain no green plants can grow: there are only bare rocks, gravel and salt. But on the fringes of the plain plant life begins. Here and there are patches of a lush green shrub—the mesquite. With their tender green leaflets, which suggest plenty of water, the plants seem completely out of place. Actually they do have a considerable source of water, but it is well underground. The mesquite has roots from 30 to 100 feet long, with which it is able to reach and tap underground lenses of fresh water fed by rain percolating down from the mountains.

The mesquite is the only shrub that can reach the water table here with its roots. But a mesquite seedling must send its roots down 30 feet or more through dry sand before it reaches this water. How, then, does it get established? This is one of the unsolved mysteries of the desert. Most of the mesquite shrubs in Death Valley are probably hundreds of years old. Some are all but buried by dunes of sand, piled around them over the years by the winds that sometimes blow with great force through the valley. There are places where dozens or hundreds of stems protrude from a dune, all probably the offshoots of a single ancient shrub rooted beneath the dune.

Another Death Valley plant endowed with a remarkable root

system is the evergreen creosote bush. It has wide-reaching roots which can extract water from a large volume of soil. The creosote bush is spread with amazingly even spacing over the desert; this is especially obvious from an airplane. The spacing apparently is due to the fact that the roots of the bush excrete toxic substances which kill any seedlings that start near it. The distance of spacing is correlated with rainfall: the less rainfall, the wider the spacing. This probably means that rain leaches the poisons from the soil so that they do not contaminate as wide an area. We commonly find young creosote bushes along roads in the desert, where the road builders have torn up the old bushes.

During prolonged periods of drought creosote bushes lose their olive-green leaves and retain only small brownish-green leaves. Eventually these also may drop off, and the bush then dies unless rain comes soon afterward. However, it takes a really long drought to kill off all the creosote bushes in an area. They have suffered severely in some areas of the southern California deserts during the drought of recent years. Because a killing drought tends to remove them wholesale, there are usually only a few age classes of creosote bushes in an area; each group springs up after a drought or during a period of unusual rainfall.

There are other shrubs that master the harsh conditions of the desert, among them the lush green *Peucephyllum,* which seems to be able to live without water, and the white-leaved desert holly, which grows in fairly salty soil.

Two prime factors control the abundance and distribution of plants: the number of seeds that germinate, and the growing conditions the seedlings encounter while they seek to establish themselves. In the case of the desert shrubs the main controlling factor is the growing conditions rather than germination, for though many seedlings may come forth in a rainy season, few survive long enough to become established. The story is entirely different for the annual plants in the desert.

148

There are years when the desert floor in Death Valley blooms with a magic carpet of color. In the spring of 1939 and again in 1947 the nonsalty portion of the valley was covered with millions of fragrant, golden-yellow desert sunflowers, spotted here and there with white evening primroses and pink desert five-spots. The bursts of flowering are not necessarily correlated with the year's rainfall. For instance, the wettest year in Death Valley was 1941, when 4.2 inches of rain fell, but there was no mass flowering that year or the following spring. If Death Valley is to bloom in the spring, the rain must come at a certain time—during the preceding November or December. There will be a mass display of spring flowers if November or December has a precipitation of well over one inch: in December of 1938 and in November of 1946 the rainfall was 1.4 inches. Rain of this magnitude in August, September, January or February seems ineffective.

Let us consider these annual plants in greater detail. Probably their most remarkable feature is that they are perfectly normal plants, with no special adaptations to withstand drought. Yet they are not found outside the desert areas. The reason lies in the peculiar cautiousness of their seeds. In dry years the seeds lie dormant. This itself is not at all amazing; what is remarkable is that they refuse to germinate even after a rain unless the rainfall is at least half an inch, and preferably an inch or two. Since the upper inch of soil, where all the viable seeds lie, is as wet after a rain of a tenth of an inch as after one of two inches, their discrimination seems hard to explain. How can a completely dormant seed measure the rainfall? That it actually does so can easily be verified in the laboratory. If seed-containing desert soil is spread on pure sand and wet with a rain sprinkler, the seeds will not germinate until the equivalent of one inch of rain has fallen on them. Furthermore, the water must come from above; no germination takes place in a container where water only soaks up from below.

Of course this sounds highly implausible—how can the direction from which the water molecules approach make any difference to the seed? The answer seems to be that water leaching down through the soil dissolves seed inhibitors. Many seeds have water-soluble germination inhibitors in their covering. They cannot germinate until the inhibitors are removed. This can be done by leaching them in a slow stream of water percolating through the soil, which is what happens during a rainstorm. Water soaking up in the soil from below of course has no leaching action. Some seeds refuse to germinate when the soil contains any appreciable amount of salt. A heavy rain, leaching out the salts, permits them to sprout. Other seeds, including those of many grasses, delay germination for a few days after a rain and then sprout if the soil is still moist—which means that the rain probably was fairly heavy. Still other seeds have inhibitors that can be removed only by the action of bacteria, which requires prolonged moisture. Many seeds preserve their dormancy until they have been wet by a series of rains.

In the washes (dry rivers) of the desert we find a completely different vegetation with different germination requirements. The seeds of many shrubs that grow exclusively in washes (paloverde, ironwood, the smoke tree) have coats so hard that only a strong force can crack them. Seeds of the paloverde can be left in water for a year without a sign of germination; but the embryo grows out within a day if the seed coat is opened mechanically. In nature such seeds are opened by the grinding action of sand and gravel. A few days after a cloudburst has dragged mud and gravel over the bottom of a wash, the bottom is covered with seedlings. It is easy to show that this germination is due to the grinding action of the mud-flow: for instance, seedlings of the smoke tree spring up not under the parent shrub itself but about 150 to 300 feet downstream. That seems to be the critical distance: seeds deposited closer to the shrub have not been ground enough to open, and those farther downstream have been pulverized. Smoke-tree seedlings form about three leaves, then stop their above-ground growth until their roots have penetrated deep enough to provide an adequate supply of moisture for the plant. Thereafter the roots grow about five times as fast as the shoots. Few of these seedlings die of drought, but a flood will destroy most of them; only the oldest and biggest shrubs resist the terrific onslaught of rocks, gravel, sand and mud streaming down the wash.

The ability of the smoke tree to make the most of the available moisture was demonstrated by the following experiment. Cracked smoke-tree seeds were sown on top of an eight-foot-high cylinder containing sand moistened with a nutrient solution. Rain water was then sprinkled on them for a short time. Six seeds germinated, and five of the plants survived and have grown for 18 months in a high temperature with only a single watering midway in that period. Indeed, they have grown better than seedlings which were watered daily!

We have studied the control of germination in great detail in our laboratory at the California Institute of Technology. We have learned, for instance, that two successive rains of three tenths of an inch will cause germination provided they are given not longer than 48 hours apart. Rain in darkness has a different effect from rain during the day. Most amazing is the seeds' specific responses to temperature. When a mixture of rain-treated seeds of various annuals is kept in a warm greenhouse, only the summer-germinating plants sprout; the seeds of the winter annuals remain dormant. When the same seed mixture is kept in a cool place, only the winter annuals germinate. From this it is obvious that the annuals will not germinate unless they can survive the temperatures following their germination—and unless there has been enough rain to allow them to complete their life cycle. Since these desert plants cannot depend on "follow-up" rains in nature, they germinate only if they have enough rain beforehand to give them a reasonable chance for survival.

A very small percentage of seeds (less than 1 per cent) germinate after an insufficient rain. Such seedlings almost invariably perish before reaching the flowering stage. On the other hand, more than 50 per cent of all seedlings that have sprouted after a heavy rain survive, flower and set seed. And here we find a remarkable fact: even though the seedlings come up so thickly that there are several thousand per square yard, a majority of them grow to maturity. Though crowded and competing for water, nutrients and light, they do not kill one another off but merely fail to grow to normal size. In one case 3,000 mature plants were found where an estimated 5,000 seedlings had originally germinated. The 3,000 belonged to 10 different species. All had remained small, but each had at least one flower and produced at least one seed. This phenomenon is not peculiar to desert plants. In fields of wheat, rice and sugar cane, at spots where seeds happen to have been sown too thickly, all the seedlings grow up together; they may be spindly but they do not die. It is true that in gardens weeds often crowd out some of the desirable plants, but usually this happens only because these plants have been sown or planted out of season or in the wrong climate. Under those conditions they cannot compete with the plants fully adapted to the local growing conditions—plants which we usually call weeds.

We must conclude, then, that all we have read about the ruthless struggle for existence and the "survival of the fittest" in nature is not necessarily true. Among many plants, especially annuals, there is no struggle between individuals for precedence or survival. Once an annual has germinated, it matures and fulfills its destiny of forming new seed. In other words, after successful germination annual plants are less subject to the process of "natural selection." Very likely this accounts for the fact that so few of the desert annuals seem to show adaptations to the desert environment. This does not mean that the plants have avoided evolution, but the evolution has operated on their seeds and methods of germination rather than on the characteristics of the grown plants. Selection on the basis of germination has endowed the plants with a remarkable variety of mechanisms for germinating, and at the same time it has made them slow to germinate except under conditions insuring their later survival. The opposite is true of the cultivated plants that man has developed: his selection has favored the plants that germinate most easily and quickly. This has given us the wrong perspective on the significance of germination in plant survival.

We return now to our original theme: Can the ecology of plants in the desert teach us anything about human ecology or human relations? At least one moral stands out. In the desert, where want and hunger for water are the normal burden of all plants, we find no fierce competition for existence, with the strong crowding out the weak. On the contrary, the available possessions —space, light, water and food—are shared and shared alike by all. If there is not enough for all to grow tall and strong, then all remain smaller. This factual picture is very different from the time-honored notion that nature's way is cutthroat competition among individuals.

Actually competition or warfare as the human species has developed it is rare in nature. Seldom do we find war between groups of individuals of the same species. There are predators, but almost always they prey on a different species; they do not practice cannibalism. The strangler fig in the tropical jungle, which kills other trees to reach the light, is a rare type, as Dobzhansky and Murça-Pires make clear in their consideration of this odd group of plants (page 131). Even in the dense forest there is little killing of the small and weak. The forest giants among the trees do not kill the small fry under them. They hold back their development, and they prevent further germination. In a mountain forest in Java it was observed that the small trees living in the shade of the forest giants had not grown after 40 years, but they were still alive.

Hundreds of different species of trees, large and small, grow in a tropical jungle. This diversity of vegetation is one of the jungle's most typical characteristics. Some trees grow faster, taller or wider than others, but these growing characteristics, which we have always considered as useful adaptations in the struggle for existence, do not really control the trees' survival. If they did, we would find very few species of trees in a jungle, and there would be an evolutionary tendency for these trees to become taller and taller. Actually the tallest trees are found not in jungles but in more open forests in temperate climates; remarkably enough, tropical jungles often have no particularly high or large trees. All this shows that selection does not work on the basis of growth potential. It works on the ability of plants to grow and survive with very little light.

In our minds the struggle for existence is usually associated with a ruthless extermination of the less well adapted by those better adapted—a sort of continuous cold war. There is no cold war or even aggression in the desert or jungle. Most plants are not equipped with mechanisms to combat others. All plants grow up together and share whatever light or water or nutrients are available. It is only when the supply of one of these factors becomes critical that competition starts. But it appears likely that in the jungle, as in the desert, survival is taken care of by the control of germination. Competition and selection occur during germination, and we can speak of germination control of the plant community—comparable to birth control in human society.

Apparently evolution has already eliminated most of the plant types that are unable to compete successfully. Fast-growing, slow-growing or tall plants all have the same chances once they have germinated. The struggle for existence is not waged among the well-established plant forms but tends to eliminate new types which germinate at inopportune times, have a decreased ability to photosynthesize or are less frost-resistant. This explains why so few plants die in the desert from drought or in the jungle from lack of light or in cold climates from frost.

As a general moral we conclude that war as man wages it finds no counterpart in nature, and it has no justification on the basis of evolution or natural selection. If we want to describe the process of control of the plant population in human terms, we should talk about birth control.

CHEMICAL SOCIOLOGY AMONG THE PLANTS

by James Bonner

Plants, like animals, do not live alone. Just as every animal's environment includes other animals, so a plant is affected by other plants in its community. There is such a thing as a sociology of plants, and a very considerable amount of attention has been given to various phases of that study. It is known that members of the plant kingdom not only compete among themselves for food, light and water but often engage in more subtle forms of warfare or co-operation. This article will deal with a remarkable phenomenon in plant relations that has only recently come to light: the fact that some plants possess chemical weapons with which they attack their neighbors.

The explanation of this phenomenon requires some preliminary consideration of the facts of plant ecology, i.e., the interrelations among plants and their environment. If we look at a plant society, we see that it is almost always made up not only of individuals of the same species but of a number of species, all growing together in more or less intimacy. It is easy enough to understand why plants of the same species should settle in the same place: they have similar requirements and all can thrive on, or at least tolerate, the physical environment of that particular habitat. But what are the factors that determine which species of plants may dwell together?

One significant clue lies in the fact that certain groups of species are likely to be found together in many sites where similar conditions prevail. So constant are these societies that it is possible to classify the groups and to name them as particular communities and associations, just as taxonomists name individual species of plants or animals. On the other hand, there are species that are never found together in the same association, even though members of these species may range widely over the same general geographic region. The citizens of the plant world, one may say, are segregated into exclusive associations which get along congenially in their own groups but do not mix with foreigners.

Obviously the most important selective factors are climate and the physical surroundings. The species that grow in association thrive on similar conditions of temperature, light, water and soil. This is particularly evident in the cases of plants that grow under unusual conditions—in bogs, in high meadows, in salty sinks, on seacoasts, in arid, rocky deserts. Undoubtedly many plant associations, perhaps all, are influenced in their species composition by this factor of site selection by the species that are best adapted to that site. A great deal of the work done in plant ecology has involved trying to find out just what the physical factors are that condition a particular plant association.

An individual plant influences the well-being of the other individuals in its association in various ways, of which the best understood is the competition for some factor essential to growth, such as light, water, or mineral elements. This might be called economic conflict. Thus limitations in soil nutrients or in soil moisture may restrict the total number of individuals that can live on a given area. Or again a tree, when it becomes established in brush vegetation, as it grows taller may rob the shrubs of light to such an extent that the latter may no longer be able to survive. These economic factors of competition vary considerably in importance, depending on whether the different species involved tend to be equal or disparate in height, on whether their roots grow through the same layer of soil or exploit different soil layers, and so on. It

157

is probably an axiom of plant sociology that a stable plant community tends to be made up of species whose individuals provide the least amount of economic competition to one another.

The method of interaction among individual plants with which we are here concerned is not, however, based on competition, at least not in the same sense. It has to do with the production by a particular species of chemical substances that are given off to the soil and influence the growth and welfare of other species. The plants that war upon one another in this way would not necessarily be in conflict so far as food or other requirements are concerned. They appear, however, to be inherently antagonistic.

In the field of microbiology this kind of phenomenon has been known for some time. We are well acquainted with a certain microscopic plant that produces poisonous substances: the fungus *Penicillium notatum,* which yields penicillin, a chemical that is highly toxic to a wide variety of other organisms. In 1932, four years after Alexander Fleming discovered penicillin, the U. S. botanist Richard Weindling found that a soil fungus named *Glyocladium* produced a substance, glyotoxin, which was toxic to the growth of other organisms, including other fungi. Scores of such antisocial chemicals have now been isolated from a wide variety of microorganisms (although only a few have all the properties needed to make them effective therapeutically in higher animals as are penicillin and streptomycin).

That higher plants also possess this property has long been suspected. Augustin de Candolle, the great Swiss botanist of the early nineteenth century, recorded that thistles appeared to inhibit the growth of oats. He suggested that this interaction might be due to specific chemical inhibitors. The first experiments specifically designed to test this hypothesis were carried out in England by S. C. Pickering and the Duke of Bedford in the early years of this century. In one type of experiment they grew apple trees in tubs moistened with water that had previously leached through pots containing growing grasses. They showed that the grasses appeared to produce in the water a substance that inhibited the growth of apple trees. In a series of brilliant investigations carried out by Oswald Schreiner and his colleagues in the United States Department of Agriculture, four different substances toxic to plant growth were isolated from various soils. In none of these early investigations, however, was there complete proof that a particular species growing in nature or in the field is inhibited by an identifiable substance produced by a second species. The evidence which led to this conclusion has been obtained only in recent years.

Perhaps the most detailed observation made was that by the German H. Bode and the Belgian G. L. Funke in the years 1939 to 1943. Bode, who worked in a garden of pharmaceutical plants, observed that along the two sides of a row of plants of the wormwood, *Artemisia absinthium,* individuals of other species grew very poorly or were killed outright. The inhibitory influence of the row of wormwood extended for upward of a meter in each direction. This growth-depressing effect could not be attributed to competition of the *Artemisia* with other plants, for other shrub species of size and habit closely comparable to wormwood exerted no such effects. Bode showed that the action of the wormwood on other plants was due to a chemical compound, absinthin, which is produced in glandular hairs on the surface of the *Artemisia* leaves. The compound is washed off onto the adjacent soil by rain, and the toxicity of the soil is constantly renewed as recurring rains bring fresh supplies of the toxic compound to it. The effect of absinthin is not the same on all species of plants. A few appear to be resistant to it. When *Artemisia absinthium* is grown in the field, Funke discovered, only these resistant species appear in the same patch; the other weed species usually found in such sites are suppressed.

Another antisocial chemical is produced by leaves of the brittlebush, *Encelia farinosa,* which inhabits the low hot deserts of the

United States Southwest. Frits W. Went, studying the flora of this region, found that most of the species of perennial shrubs growing there harbor a vigorous coterie of annuals around them, no doubt in part at least because they provide shade and an accumulation of organic matter for the lesser plants. The brittlebush, however, is a conspicuous exception. The area under and around a brittlebush is in general barren of other plants except in certain special circumstances. Because the absence of other plants did not appear to be due to simple competition effects, fallen leaves of the brittlebush were scraped from the ground under the bush and taken to a laboratory for study. When they were placed as a mulch over sand in pots in which tomatoes or other species were growing, it was found that the brittlebush leaves, even in small quantities, caused severe retardation of growth, or even the death, of the test plant.

The toxic action of *Encelia* leaves, like that of *Absinthium*, is highly specific. It has little effect on the brittlebush itself, on sunflowers, or on barley; but it has a pronounced influence on certain other plants, notably, as has been mentioned, the tomato. On chemical fractionation, the *Encelia* leaves yielded a toxic compound which, isolated in crystalline form, was found to be a new chemical substance, 3-acetyl-6-methoxy benzaldehyde. This compound, when synthesized in the laboratory, had a toxic activity identical with that of the natural material. Experiments have shown that the fallen leaves of the brittlebush retain their toxicity for a year or more in the absence of rain, and that the toxic material is leached out into the soil by water. Annuals usually associated with shrubs, such as *Rafinesquia*, are highly susceptible to the brittlebush toxic substance. It may therefore be concluded that the lack of growth of annuals in association with *Encelia* under natural conditions may be due to the production by brittlebush of this toxic substance. An exceptional situation occurs, however, in certain mountainous areas where *Encelia* grows on steep slopes that are subject to occasional torrential runoff. There the ground under the plant is free of the mulch of fallen leaves, and it is not uncommon to find individuals of several other species growing in association with the shrub.

It has been known for many years that the black walnut (*Juglans nigra*) exerts a detrimental effect on the growth of surrounding plants of many species, and it has often been suggested that this may be due to a chemical substance produced by the tree. Everett Davis, working in West Virginia, sought to determine whether the injurious effects produced by the black walnut derived from juglone, a compound found in the foliage and roots of the plant. He showed that juglone is toxic to tomato and alfalfa plants. It has not been proved, however, that juglone is in fact the means by which the black walnut injures other plants under natural conditions. This case remains to be worked out in detail, and it is of interest to do so because of the prevalence of black walnut poisoning of crops in the East and Southwest.

Chemical interaction is not restricted to plants of different species. We know that in some instances a plant may produce a compound which is inhibitory to plants of its own species. Such a plant is the guayule, *Parthenium argentatum,* a rubber-bearing shrub of the southwest desert. When this plant is grown under laboratory conditions, the roots give off a substance that is toxic to seedlings of the same species. The inhibitor was isolated in pure form and shown to be cinnamic acid. This substance has a powerful effect: less than one part in 200,000 parts of soil is sufficient to bring about a significant depression of seedling growth.

Why should a plant produce a compound highly toxic to its own species and much less toxic to other species? An answer to this question may perhaps be found in the way in which shrubby species are distributed under desert conditions. Normally in such an environment the individuals of a given species are widely and uniformly spaced, as though to share the scant supplies of water and nutrients. Seedlings of guayule are rarely found under a mature guayule plant—a situation common to a wide range of desert shrubs. Even when guayule seedlings are transplanted into the neighborhood of a mature guayule plant they show poor survival and little growth. It can be shown by experiment that this failure is directly related to the inhibitor produced by the mature plant. The explanation may be that the mature guayule plant produces its inhibitor to prevent the establishment of young competitors for water and food.

The chemical interaction between plants is not always hostile. There are plants that produce substances which promote the growth of other plants instead of inhibiting it. Certain leguminous plants excrete nitrogenous compounds which may be taken up and used by associated nonleguminous species. Went has shown that in the tropical rain forest of Java each species of forest tree has its own particular species of epiphytes, higher plants whose seeds germinate and grow high up on the trunk of the host. This specificity of epiphyte for host tree may be a reflection of the effects of particular compounds from the tree on the germination and growth of the seeds of the epiphyte species.

It is clear that further and more detailed investigations are necessary in order to discover the exact limits of chemical interaction among higher plants. It appears that the production of substances inhibitory to other plants may be very widespread in the plant world. In a survey of native woody species of one section of eastern California alone, it was found that the leaves of approximately half of the species collected contained principles toxic to the growth of one selected test plant.

Fundamentally, of course, the chemical interactions among plants must have something to do with the factor of competition, which is undoubtedly of the most general and pervasive significance in plant relations. Thus chemical warfare and co-operation are merely one phase of the larger complex of interactions which determine the sociology of the plant community.

THE FERTILIZATION OF
FLOWERS
by Verne Grant

Wʜᴀᴛ is a flower? How is it constructed, how does it function, how did flowers originate and evolve into the more than 150,000 species found on earth? Although man has always lived in a world of flowers, as recently as 200 years ago their biological meaning was still a mystery. Today, thanks to two centuries of patient work by many botanists all over the world, the mystery is to some extent explained.

Flowers are the reproductive structures of plants. The structures consist of pollen-bearing stamens (the male organs) and carpels (the female organs) containing pollen-catching stigmas and ovules, the plant's "eggs." A union of the pollen with the ovules produces seeds. Most of the flowers with which we are familiar have both organs, the stamens and the carpels, in the same flower. It would be most convenient for the plant if each flower's pollen fertilized its own ovules, but many flowers cannot pollinate themselves. They are fertilized by pollen from other individuals of the same species. From an evolutionary standpoint this has advantages, for it produces a combination of different heredities and yields more variable and more flexible progeny.

In the animal kingdom this kind of union poses no special difficulties. Impelled by an urge to mate, the male and female swim, crawl, walk or fly until they find each other. But the union of two flowering plants, anchored by their roots to separate spots of ground, presents a problem that can be solved only by the intervention of some third party. The pollen of one plant must be carried to the ovules of the other by an external agent—the wind, water currents, an insect or some other animal. Obviously if this is to occur it must be advantageous or inevitable for that agent to carry the pollen. In the long course of evolution the flowers of plants have become adapted through natural selection to the characteristics of their pollinators. Thus the various species of flowers owe their structure, shape, color, odor and other attributes to the particular agents that cross-pollinate them. The flowers of the earth group themselves into several broad classes depending on how they are pollinated. There are the bee flowers, the moth flowers, the fly flowers, the beetle flowers, the bird flowers, the bat flowers, the wind flowers, and so on.

The bee flowers include some orchids, verbena, violets, blue columbine, larkspur, monkshood, bleeding heart, many members of the mint, snapdragon and pea families, and a host of others. All of them offer nectar as a reward to the bees, and all advertise their presence by showy, brightly colored petals and a sweet fragrance. The bee flowers and bees are beautifully adapted to each other in biological construction and habits. Most bee flowers are blue or yellow or some mixture of these two colors, and experiments show that the vision of bees is mainly in this part of the spectrum; they are color-blind to red. Bees respond to sweet,

Fertilization of flowers is illustrated by these partially diagrammatic drawings of the apricot flower. The top drawing shows the fresh blossom. One pollen grain from an open stamen has fallen on the pistil. Fertilization takes place *(bottom drawing)* when the pollen tube growing from the pollen grain makes its way down through the carpel to enter the ovule and a sperm nucleus unites with an egg nucleus to produce a new seed, or fruit. In the bottom drawing this begins to grow. By then some petals have fallen and the stamens withered.

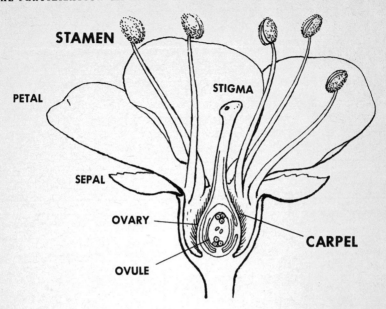

STAMEN

PETAL

STIGMA

SEPAL

OVARY

CARPEL

OVULE

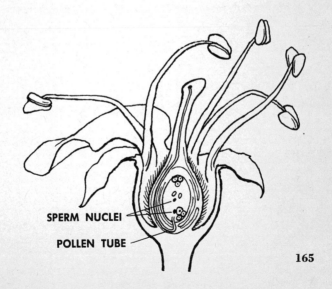

SPERM NUCLEI

POLLEN TUBE

165

aromatic or minty odors and apparently are not stimulated at all by foul ones. Bees fly only by day, and bee flowers are always open in daytime but often closed at night.

In visiting a flower a bee habitually alights first on a petal. Many bee flowers provide a protruding lip as a landing platform. The bee then pushes its way into the region of nectar and pollen. Bee flowers secrete nectar from special glands which often lie at the base of a tube of petals. Bees, with their long, slender tongues, can reach the nectar, but most other insects cannot. As the bee takes the nectar, its body hairs inevitably pick up pollen from the flower's stamens. In some bee flowers the stamens have special lever, trigger or piston devices for dusting pollen on some particular spot of the bee's body. When the bee has finished working on one flower, it flies rapidly on to another. Bees have an instinct to confine their attention to flowers of one species at a time; they recognize a species by its characteristic odor, form and color. This is very convenient for the flower, since it assures that the bee will deliver its load of pollen where it will do the most good, namely, to another flower of the same species which the pollen can fertilize. Since the stamens and carpels are grouped together in the flower, the bee simultaneously delivers its load of pollen to the carpels and picks up a new load from the stamens at each visit. It delivers enough pollen grains to fertilize a large number of ovules, and most bee-pollinated plants do in fact ripen numerous seeds in each flower.

Bee flowers thrive best in sunny and arid or semi-arid parts of temperate regions, where bees find the climatic conditions to their liking. Many bee-pollinated plants are unable to reproduce themselves in areas that lack certain kinds of bees. For example, monkshood, a bumblebee flower, does not occur naturally outside the range of bumblebees in the Northern Hemisphere. Alfalfa, a cultivated species of the pea family, is often infertile in California, where the proper kinds of bees are scarce under the highly artificial conditions of cultivation.

The moth and butterfly flowers also are very numerous. Among the moth flowers are the morning-glory, tobacco, yellow columbine, datura, white catchfly, yucca, phlox, some evening primroses and many orchids; the butterfly flowers include the carnation, red catchfly and many lilies. Nearly all species of moths and butterflies have a long tongue for sucking nectar; in tropical hawk moths the tongue is sometimes as long as 25 centimeters. Unlike bees, moths do not settle down on the flower during feeding; they hover above it with the tongue inserted in the nectar. They are guided to flowers by a combination of sight and smell, but most of them fly during dusk and at night, so that moth flowers run mainly to white shades and a very heavy fragrance. Many of these flowers open only in the late afternoon or evening and are closed through the hours of bright sunshine. Butterfly flowers, on the other hand, often have red or orange colors, since butterflies feed during the daytime and some of them, unlike bees, can see the red part of the spectrum.

The nectar of moth and butterfly flowers is secreted at the base of a long slender floral tube, where it is accessible only to the long-tongued moths and butterflies. In many species of moths the length of the tongue closely matches the length of the tube in the particular flower that the species visits. Like bees, moths and butterflies tend to feed on one kind of flower at a time.

Moth flowers apparently are most plentiful in tropical and warm temperate latitudes. They are common at high elevation on temperate mountain ranges, but are absent from the Arctic and Antarctic.

The flies that feed on flowers fall into two classes: long-tongued and short-tongued. The long-tongued flies, such as the syrphids and bombylids, in the main visit the same types of flowers as bees, since they are well adapted in bodily structure, habits and sensory perception to live on the nectar of these flowers. The truly distinctive fly flowers, therefore, are those that feed the short-tongued flies.

These flies, consisting of some 30 or more families, are a diverse and miscellaneous lot, and they have no particular specializations for feeding on flowers. Most of them probably derive their nourishment mainly from other sources, notably carrion, dung, humus, sap and blood. The flowers that attract them are those that carry similar odors. Unlike bees, moths and long-tongued flies, the short-tongued flies are attracted to flowers not primarily by vision but by their sense of smell. The fly flowers, consequently, are generally dull of color and rank in odor. Rafflesia, a large-blossomed fly flower of Malaysia, smells like putrefying flesh; another fly flower, black arum, has the odor of human dung; another, the lily *Scoliopus bigelovii,* smells like fish oil; there is a species of Dutchman's-pipe that smells like decaying tobacco and another that smells like humus.

The performance of short-tongued flies on flowers may be described as unindustrious, unskilled and stupid. Some fly flowers obtain the pollen-carrying services of flies without even expending any nectar on them. In this case the flies are attracted to special glistening streaks, spots or bodies, as in the saxifrage *Parnassia,* the lily *Paris* and the orchid *Ophrys.* The flowers of Dutchman's-pipe and arum not only fail to feed the flies but actually imprison them for a day or two in a floral trap while they are being doused with pollen. After the flies escape from one flower, they may go on to a second trap, where they have the opportunity during another day or two to pollinate the flower thoroughly.

The American floral ecologist John Lovell once remarked upon the vast difference in the reception that flowers accord to bees and to flies. The efficient and constant bees are offered nectar, pollen, shelter, a landing platform, bright colors and sweet odors, and their competitors for the limited supply of food are excluded from the floral chamber. For the stupid flies, on the other hand, there are pitfalls, prisons, pinch-traps and deceptive nectaries!

Fly flowers are especially common in plants of arctic and high mountainous regions where other types of animal-pollinated flowers are infrequent or absent. They are also found in shady woods of the temperate and tropical zones.

The beetle flowers also attract their insect pollen-carriers chiefly by odor rather than by sight. The flower-visiting beetles with rare exceptions are not specially adapted for feeding on flowers and may derive most of their nourishment from other sources, such as sap, fruit, leaves, dung and carrion. They may be attracted to flowers by fruity, spicy or sweet odors. There are two general types of beetle flowers. One group has large, solitary blossoms; among them are magnolias, pond lilies, California poppy, sweet shrub (Calycanthus) and wild rose. The other has clusters of small flowers; examples in this group are dogwood, elder, spirea, buck-thorn and some members of the arum, parsley and sunflower families.

The beetles not only lap up the nectar and other juices of a flower but also feed on the tissues of petals and stamens. To pro-tect the ovules from the chewing jaws of their pollinators, most beetle flowers have the ovules well buried beneath the floral chamber. Several of them hold the beetles in a trap while the stig-mas receive pollen and the stamens sprinkle a fresh supply onto the bodies of the prisoners. They then open up an exit by which the beetle escapes. On the other hand, many beetle flowers have a shallow, open basin freely accessible to all comers. This makes them a common camping ground for many other kinds of small insects, including flies, wasps, bugs and bees.

Beetle flowers are most abundant in tropical latitudes and diminish toward the colder parts of the earth.

It is a common notion that insects are by far the most important animal pollinators of flowers, but actually in some parts of the world, particularly in the tropics and Southern Hemisphere, birds may be even more important. Hummingbirds in North and South America, sunbirds in Africa and Asia, honey eaters and lorikeets in Australia, honey creepers in the Hawaiian Islands, and several other groups of birds regularly visit flowers to feed on nectar, flower-inhabiting insects and pollen.

Birds have powerful vision and only a feebly developed sense of smell, so the bird flowers rely mainly on color to attract their pollinators. Most of them are large and colorful and many are odorless. The sensitivity of the bird's eye, like that of man, is great in the red end of the spectrum but relatively weak in the region of blue and violet. Hence the most frequent colors in bird flowers are red and yellow. The bird flowers include red columbine, fuchsia, passionflower, eucalyptus, hibiscus and members of the pea, cactus, pineapple, banana and orchid families. Bird flowers are most common in tropical and warm temperate latitudes.

Hummingbirds commonly suck the nectar of flowers on the wing, and the flowers that they visit most often are of the hanging type. On the other hand, the flowers favored by sunbirds, which settle on the plant, usually stand erect and provide a landing platform. A bird probes into the chamber of a flower with its sharp-pointed bill. This frequently causes considerable mechanical damage to the inner floral parts. The bird flowers therefore put their ovules out of harm's way in an ovary under the floral chamber, behind a sheath or at the end of a special stalk.

The petals of bird flowers are fused into a tube which holds copious quantities of thin nectar. The proportions of the tube often correspond to the length and curvature of the bird's bill. The stamens are usually brightly colored, numerous and turned out so that they touch the bird on the breast or head while it feeds. The pollen adheres in sticky masses or threads. A single pollinating visit thus suffices for the fertilization of scores or hundreds of ovules. The importance of birds as pollinators is indicated by the fact that the Mexican century-plant, whose pollen is carried by hummingbirds, is barren when transplanted to Europe, where hummingbirds are absent. The flower is abundantly visited by bees, but without hummingbirds it remains sterile.

The bat flowers are pollinated by certain species of tropical bats with long, slender muzzles, extensile tongues and shortened or missing front teeth—all adaptations that enable the bats to feed on flowers. They feed at night and are probably guided to the flowers chiefly by their well-developed sense of smell. They clamber on the flower, hold on with their claws and extract nectar or small insects from the floral chamber with the tongue or chew the pollen or succulent petals. The tree-borne bat flowers of the tropics are large, frequently dirty white in color and open only at night. They attract the bats by a fermenting or fruitlike odor, which is given off at night. Examples of bat flowers are calabash, sausage tree, candle tree and some other members of the trumpet-vine family, various members of the sapodilla family and areca palm.

The flowers pollinated by the wind need no bright colors, special odors, nectar or other attractions, and they have none. Most of them even lack petals. Instead their stamens and stigmas are exposed as freely as possible to the air currents, and they provide huge masses of light, smooth-skinned pollen that can be scattered far and wide. Pollen grains borne by the wind have been collected in air traps over the middle of the Atlantic, hundreds of miles from their source.

Because there is no special advantage to be had in grouping stamens and carpels together in the same flower, as in animal-pollinated plants, the sexes in the wind flowers are often separated into staminate and carpellate flowers, which are borne either in different parts of the plant or on different individual plants. The stigma is feathery, brushy or fleshy, so that the wind-carried pollen will stick to it. The pollen grains of a wind flower, being borne thinly in the air, land singly on a stigma and not in masses as with animal-borne pollen. Each act of pollination thus leads to the fertilization of one ovule in each flower. Most wind-pollinated plants have become adapted to this condition by producing single-seeded fruits: the oak flower produces one acorn, the grass flower one grain.

Wind flowers are most common in the Arctic and Antarctic, where most insects cannot live, and also play a very important role in the cold temperate zones. Among the wind-pollinated plants are the grasses, sedges, rushes, cattail, dock, goosefoot, hemp, nettle, plantain, alder, hazel, birch, oak and poplar.

Many flowers, of course, fall into more than one category. Corn plants, for example, are pollinated primarily by wind but visited also by bees. Some European heaths are pollinated by bees in the spring but cease producing nectar and commit their pollen to the wind at the end of the season. Phlox flowers, normally pollinated by moths, may occasionally be fertilized by thrips. Some European species of gentian and violet are pollinated by bees in the lowlands and by butterflies in the Alps. Similar variations occur among the different species in a genus or family of plants. In short, the classes are not static. Changes in the method of pollination have occurred with considerable frequency during the history of the earth. These changes, and the nice adaptation of the flowers to their pollinators, show clearly that the pollinating agents have played a major active role in the evolution of flowers.

The fossil record indicates that flowers originated sometime during the middle of the Mesozoic Era, about 150 million years ago. Flowers, like mammals and birds, probably made their first humble appearance in the age of conifers, cycads, dinosaurs and beetles. Most of the seed-bearing plants of that age were probably pollinated by wind. They possessed the same kinds of reproductive structures, including separate sexes and in some instances winged pollen, that are associated with wind pollination in their modern survivors. The ovules were borne in cones or on leaves and exuded drops of sap. In the course of time beetles, feeding on the sap and resin of stems and on leaves, must have discovered that the liquid droplets from the ovules and the pollen in the male cones were nutritious foods. Some of these beetles, returning regularly to the newly found source of food, would have accidentally carried pollen to the ovules. For some Mesozoic plants this new method of pollination may have represented a more efficient method of cross-pollination than the releasing of enormous quantities of pollen into the air. Through natural selection they would develop adaptations to the potentialities of beetle pollination. The ovules, first of all, must be placed behind some protective wall to prevent their being chewed up by the beetles. One means of accomplishing this would be to fold the ovule-bearing leaf or branch into a hollow, closed carpel. The pollen-collecting function would then have to be transferred from the individual ovules to a central stigma serving all the ovules in the carpel.

The beetles could be drawn to the stigma by a special secretion of nectar which would replace the droplets previously given off by the individual ovules. A beetle visiting the stigma would be apt to leave behind sufficient pollen for the fertilization of numerous ovules. The number of seeds formed in a single pollination would no longer be one, as in the wind-pollinated ancestor, but 10 or 20. So the transition from wind to beetle pollination would increase the fertility of the plant.

The chances that the beetle would bring pollen to the stigma would be increased if the stamens were in close proximity to the carpels. The stamens and carpels might even be advantageously grouped within the same cone. The stamens would have to be present in large numbers so that they would not all be devoured

173

by the beetles. In the course of time the outer stamens might become sterilized and pigmented and transformed into a set of showy petals. When these conditions had been fulfilled, there would have come into existence a structure possessing all the essentials of a modern flower.

This, in all likelihood, is how the evolution of flowers began. The most primitive type of flower of which we have any knowledge is a beetle flower, and it seems altogether probable that the selective factor that called flowers into being was beetle pollination. From these early flowers probably are descended most of those modern families that have separate petals and open nectar. When the bees, moths, butterflies and syrphid flies arrived on the earth at the beginning of the Tertiary Period, some 70 million years ago, the evolution of flowers was greatly broadened. In flowers pollinated by the long-tongued insects the petals became fused into a tubular corolla with a supply of nectar concealed at its base. The carpels were similarly fused into a compound ovary with a more localized and centralized stigma. The tubular structure of the corolla tended to screen out the beetles and small flies and restrict visitors to those insects—the bees, moths and long-tongued flies—that fly regularly from flower to flower of the same species. This was a great step forward in floral design: it marked a transition from promiscuous pollination by miscellaneous unspecialized insects to restricted pollination by specialized and flower-constant animals.

PART 7 APPLIED GENETICS

I. WHEAT
by Paul C. Mangelsdorf
II. THE MYSTERY OF CORN
by Paul C. Mangelsdorf
III. HYBRID CORN
by Paul C. Mangelsdorf

One of the leading workers in the United States on the genetics of crop plants, Paul C. Mangelsdorf can trace his interest in this field back to early childhood. His father was a Kansas florist and seedsman. Young Mangelsdorf studied wheat- and corn-breeding at Kansas State College and after graduation in 1921 went to the Connecticut Agricultural Experiment Station as an assistant geneticist. He worked there under Donald M. Jones and took graduate work at Harvard under Edward M. East—these two played major parts in the development of hybrid corn. From 1926 to 1940 Mangelsdorf was agronomist at the Texas Agricultural Experiment Station, where he produced hybrid corn strains for the Texas climate and developed new varieties of wheat, oats and barley. He went to Harvard in 1940 and is now professor of botany and director of the Harvard Botanical Museum. Since 1941 Mangelsdorf has been Consultant for Agriculture with the Rockefeller Foundation, helping underdeveloped countries produce more corn and wheat.

WHEAT

by Paul C. Mangelsdorf

Wᴴᴱᴀᴛ is the world's most widely cultivated plant. The wheat plants growing on the earth may even outnumber those of any other seed-bearing land species, wild or domesticated. Every month of the year a crop of wheat is maturing somewhere in the world. It is the major crop of the United States and Canada and is grown on substantial acreages in almost every country of Latin America, Europe and Asia.

Apparently this grain was one of the earliest plants cultivated by man. Carbonized kernels of wheat were found recently by the University of Chicago archaeologist Robert Braidwood at the 6,700-year-old site of Jarmo in eastern Iraq, the oldest village yet discovered—a village which may have been one of the birthplaces of man's agriculture. Through the courtesy of Dr. Braidwood I have had an opportunity to study some of these ancient kernels and compare them with modern kernels, carbonized to simulate the archaeological specimens. The resemblance between the ancient and modern grains is remarkable. There were two types of kernels in the Jarmo site; one turned out to be almost identical with a wild wheat still growing in the Near East, and the other almost exactly like present-day cultivated wheat of the type called einkorn. Evidently there has been no appreciable change in these wheats in the 7,000 years since Jarmo.

When he domesticated wheat, man laid the foundations of Western civilization. No civilization worthy of the name has ever been founded on any agricultural basis other than the cereals. The ancient cultures of Babylonia and Egypt, of Rome and

Greece, and later those of northern and western Europe, were all based upon the growing of wheat, barley, rye and oats. Those of India, China and Japan had rice for their basic crop. The pre-Columbian peoples of America—Inca, Maya and Aztec—looked to corn for their daily bread.

What are the reasons for this intimate relation between the cereals and civilization? It may be primarily a question of nutrition. The grain of cereal grasses, a nutlike structure with a thin shell covering the seed, contains not only the embryo of a new plant but also a food supply to nourish it. Cereal grains, like eggs and milk, are foodstuffs designed by nature for the nutrition of the young of the species. They represent a five-in-one food supply which contains carbohydrates, proteins, fats, minerals and vitamins. A whole-grain cereal, if its food values are not destroyed by the over-refinement of modern processing methods, comes closer than any other plant product to providing an adequate diet. Man long ago discovered this fact and learned to exploit it. Guatemalan Indians manage to subsist fairly well on a diet which is 85 per cent corn. In India people sometimes live on almost nothing but rice. Such diets do not meet the approval of modern nutritionists, but they are better than those made up too largely of starchy root crops such as potatoes, sweet potatoes or cassava, or of proteinaceous legumes such as beans, peas and lentils.

Perhaps the relationship between cereals and civilization is also a product of the discipline which cereals impose upon their growers. The cereals are grown only from seed and must be planted and harvested in their proper season. In this respect they differ from the root crops, which in mild climates can be planted and harvested at almost any time of the year. Root-crop agriculture can be practiced by semi-nomadic peoples who visit their plantations only periodically. The growing of cereals has always been accompanied by a stable mode of life. Moreover, it forced men to become more conscious of the seasons and the movements of the sun, moon and stars. In both the Old World and the New the science of astronomy was invented by cereal growers, and with it a calendar and a system of arithmetic. Cereal agriculture in providing a stable food supply created leisure, and leisure in turn fostered the arts, crafts and sciences. It has been said that "cereal agriculture, alone among the forms of food production, taxes, recompenses and stimulates labor and ingenuity in an equal degree."

Today wheat is the cereal *par excellence* for breadmaking, and it is used almost exclusively for that purpose. But it is quite unlikely that breadmaking, a complex and sophisticated art, came suddenly into full flower with the domestication of wheat. Man may have begun by merely parching or popping the grain to make it edible. Primitive wheats, like other cereals, were firmly enclosed in husks, called glumes. Heating makes the glumes easy to rub off and allows the kernel itself to be more easily chewed or ground into meal. The scorching and parching of grains is still practiced on unripened cereals in parts of the Near East. In Scotland until recently barley glumes were sometimes removed by setting fire to the unthreshed heads. The Chippewa Indians still prepare wild rice by heating the unhusked kernels and tramping on them in a hollow log.

Hard-textured cereal grains with a certain moisture content explode and escape from their glumes when heated. In America the first use of corn was undoubtedly by popping. The earliest known corn had small vitreous kernels, and archaeological remains of popped corn have been found in early sites in both North and South America. In India certain varieties of rice are popped by stirring the kernels in hot sand. Many villages in India have a village popper who performs this service for his neighbors and provides himself with food by taking his toll of the product.

The botanical as well as archaeological evidence, though

179

meager, indicates that wheat was first used as a parched cereal. The dwellings at Jarmo contain ovens which prove that this primitive economy knew the controlled use of heat. All the very ancient prehistoric kernels so far found are carbonized as if they had been over-parched. In itself this evidence is not telling, since only carbonized grains would be preserved indefinitely, but it is in harmony with other evidence. Finally, the most ancient wheats are species whose kernels would not be removed from the husks merely by threshing. The simplest method of husking them to make them edible would have been parching.

Probably the second stage in progress was to grind the parched grains and soak the coarse meal in water to make a gruel. For the toothless, both old and young, this must have been a life-saving invention. Gruel or porridge is well known as a primitive form of food. A gruel prepared from parched barley was the principal food of the common people of ancient Greece. American Indians prepared a kind of porridge from corn which has its modern counterpart in "mush" and "polenta."

A gruel allowed to stand for a few days in a warm dwelling would become infected with wild yeasts. Fermenting the small amounts of sugar in cereal, the yeasts would have produced a mild alcoholic beverage. This would have pointed the way to leavened bread. It is questionable which art developed first— brewing or breadmaking. Some students believe that brewing is older even than agriculture, but there is no supporting archaeological or historical evidence. On the contrary, the earliest Egyptian recipes for beer described a process in which the grain was first made into half-baked loaves, which then became the raw material for beer-making. There is no doubt that brewing and the making of leavened bread are closely related arts, both depending upon fermentation by yeasts.

Modern breadmaking, however, had to await the appearance

of new types of wheat. It is as much a product of the evolution of wheat as it is one of human ingenuity.

Wheat differs from most cultivated plants in the complexity of its variations. True, the other major cereals, rice and corn, are each differentiated into thousands of varieties, but these form a continuous spectrum of variation and hence are classed as a single botanical species. Wheat is separated into distinct groups which differ from one another in many ways and are therefore classified as separate species under the single Old World genus *Triticum*. The domesticated wheats and their wild relatives have been studied more intensively than any other group of plants, cultivated or wild, and from these studies, truly international in scope, a picture is beginning to emerge of the evolution of wheat under domestication.

Authorities differ on the number of distinct species of wheat. This article follows the classification of Nikolai Vavilov, the Russian geneticist and botanist who, with his colleagues, brought together for study more than 31,000 samples of wheat from all parts of the world. Vavilov recognized 14 species; other botanists have recognized fewer or more. All authorities agree, however, that the wheat species, whatever their number, fall into three distinct groups, determined by the number of chromosomes in their cells. The chromosome numbers (in the reproductive cells) of the three types are, respectively, 7, 14 and 21. They were discovered by T. Sakamura in Japan in 1918 and slightly later, but independently, by Karl Sax in the United States. The numbers are closely associated with differences in anatomy, morphology, resistance to disease, productiveness, and milling and baking qualities. It is interesting to note that August Schulz, a German botanist, had arranged the wheats into these three groups in 1913, well before their chromosome numbers were known.

The 14- and 21-chromosome wheats have all arisen from 7-

chromosome wheat and related grasses, through hybridization followed by chromosome doubling. This "cataclysmic evolution" is the only known mechanism by which new true-breeding species can be created almost overnight.

Since different wild grasses have been involved in wheat's evolution, the species differ not only in the number but also in the nature of their chromosomes. Relationships of different sets of chromosomes are determined by studying the degree of chromosome pairing in the reproductive cells of hybrids. If the pairing is complete, or almost so, the chromosome sets (genoms) of the parents are regarded as identical or closely related. If there is no pairing, the parental genoms are considered to be distinct. Four different genoms, each comprising seven chromosomes, designated A, B, D and G, are recognized in wild and cultivated wheats.

Another important difference in wheats is in their heads. Primitive cereals and many wild grasses have heads whose central stem is brittle and fragile, breaking apart when mature and providing a natural mechanism for seed dispersal. When such cereals are threshed, the heads break up into individual spikelets (clusters of one or more individual grass flowers) in which the kernels remain firmly enclosed in their husks. Under domestication this characteristic, so essential to perpetuation of the species in the wild, has been lost. New forms have evolved, not only in wheat but in other cereals, in which the stems are tough and the heads remain intact when mature. In such cereals threshing alone removes the kernels from their glumes. The cereals with free-threshing, naked grains are much more useful to man, especially for milling and baking, than those that cling stubbornly to their husks. In wheats, therefore, the naked varieties have almost completely superseded the primitive forms.

The 7-chromosome wheats, probably the most ancient, consist of two species: *T. aegilopoides* and *T. monococcum,* known as wild einkorn and einkorn. Carbonized kernels of both were found at Jarmo, but whether they are the only wheats occurring in this ancient village site remains to be seen. Both species of einkorn have fragile stems and firm-hulled seeds. Their spikelets contain but a single seed, hence their name. Each has the same set of chromosomes, genom A, and they hybridize easily together to produce highly fertile offspring. Cultivated einkorn has slightly larger kernels than the wild form and a slightly tougher stem. Its heads do not fall apart quite so easily when ripe. Except for these slight differences the two species are essentially identical, and einkorn is undoubtedly the domesticated counterpart of the wild species. Apparently little significant change has been wrought in them over the centuries.

Wild einkorn has its center of distribution in Armenia and Georgia of the Soviet Union, and in Turkey. It also occurs in the eastern Caucasus and in western Iran. Westward from Asia Minor it is a common grass on the sides of low hills in Greece and Bulgaria and a weed in the well-drained vineyards of southern Yugoslavia. Cultivated einkorn originated, according to Vavilov, in the mountains of northeastern Turkey and the southwestern Caucasus. However, if my identification of the kernels at Jarmo is correct, and if Jarmo represents the beginnings of agriculture, einkorn may have been domesticated first slightly farther south in eastern Iraq. Certainly it is an ancient cereal. Carbonized grains of it have been found in neolithic deposits of the lake-dwellers and in many other sites in central and northeastern Europe. Impressions of einkorn have been identified in neolithic pottery in Britain and Ireland. There are no records of its prehistoric occurrence in India, China or Africa.

Einkorn is still grown in some parts of Europe and the Middle East, usually in hilly regions with thin soils. Its yields are low, usually not more than 8 to 15 bushels per acre. A bread, dark brown in color but of good flavor, can be made from it if it is husked, but it is more commonly used as a whole grain, like barley, for feeding cattle and horses. Einkorn's importance lies not in its present use but in its progeny. It is the ancestor of all other cultivated wheats, with the possible exception of the type called emmer. Einkorn's descendants all have in common the set of seven chromosomes called genom A.

In the next stage of evolution are the 14-chromosome species, of which Vavilov recognized seven. All these have come from the hybridization and chromosome doubling of a 7-chromosome wheat with a 7-chromosome related wild grass. The wheat parent in each case was undoubtedly einkorn, or possibly in one instance its wild relative, since all the species possess the genom A. But the wild-grass parent remains to this day unidentified and is the chief botanical mystery in the origin of cultivated wheats. This parent contributed a genom B to all in the group except one species (see diagram opposite). Edgar McFadden and Ernest Sears of the United States Department of Agriculture have suggested that genom B may have been derived from a species of *Agropyron,* a genus of weedy grasses which includes the pernicious couch grass of the northeastern United States. Only one of the 14-chromosome wheats is found wild. This species, which is called wild emmer, is indigenous to southern Armenia, northeastern Turkey, western Iran, Syria and northern Palestine.

Closely resembling wild emmer, and possibly derived directly from it by domestication, is emmer, the oldest of 14-chromosome cultivated wheats and once the most widely grown wheat of all. An alternative possibility, however, is that emmer is the product of hybridization between einkorn and a 7-chromosome wild relative. The fact that crosses of wild and cultivated emmer are sometimes partly sterile indicates that the two forms may not be closely related and that one may be the product of an ancient hybridization and the other of a more recent one. There is at least no doubt

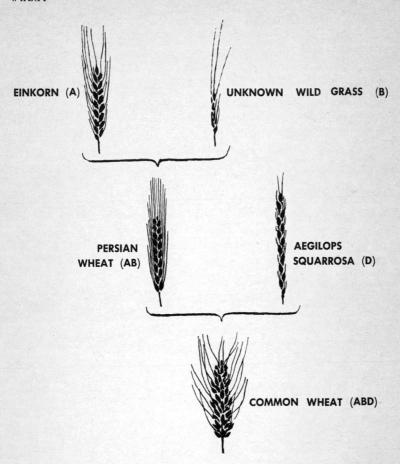

EINKORN (A)

UNKNOWN WILD GRASS (B)

PERSIAN WHEAT (AB)

AEGILOPS SQUARROSA (D)

COMMON WHEAT (ABD)

Ancestry of common wheat, to the extent that it is known, is charted in this family tree. Domestic einkorn, selected from wild einkorn and carrying the 7-chromosome gene constellation A, was crossed with a wild grass carrying the 7-chromosome genom B to give rise to the Persian wheat with 14 chromosomes combining A and B. The crossing of Persian wheat with another wild grass, *Aegilops squarrosa* with the 7-chromosome genom D, yielded common wheat carrying the 21-chromosome genom ABD.

about the antiquity of emmer. Well-preserved spikelets scarcely different from those of modern emmer have been found in Egyptian tombs of the Fifth Dynasty. Emmer may well have been the chief cereal of the Near East from very early times to the Greco-Roman period, for until the Jarmo find it was the only wheat found archaeologically in early sites of that region. Remains or impressions of it have also been common in neolithic sites in continental Europe, Britain and Ireland.

Emmer, like einkorn, has a fragile stem and clinging hull. Good bread and fine cake and pastry can be made from it, but most emmer today is fed to livestock. Some varieties are quite resistant to stem and leaf rust, the principal diseases of wheat, and have been useful in plant breeding.

The 14-chromosome wheats were the first to produce species with tough stems and with kernels that thresh free from their glumes. Four such species are known: *durum* (macaroni), *persicum* (Persian), *turgidum* (rivet) and *polonicum* (Polish). All have a more recent history than einkorn or emmer. The oldest, durum, first appeared in the Greco-Roman period about the first century B.C. One of the most recent, Polish wheat, unique for its massive heads and long, hard kernels, did not appear until the seventeenth century. None of these wheats except durum is of great commercial importance today. Durum wheat, the best variety for the manufacture of macaroni, spaghetti and other edible paste products, is grown fairly extensively in Italy, Spain and parts of the United States. Rivet wheat is of some interest because it is the tallest-growing (four to six feet high) and under ideal conditions one of the most productive. However, its grains are soft, yielding a weak flour unsuitable for breadmaking unless mixed with stronger wheats. One variety of rivet called "miracle" or "mummy" wheat, with massive branched heads, has been persistently exploited as a rare and valuable wheat claimed to have been propagated from prehistoric grains discovered in ancient Egyptian tombs, usually in the wrappings of a mummy. The story in all of its versions is a complete fabrication. Wheat kernels, like seeds of other plants, are living metabolic systems with a maximum life expectancy of about 10 years. Furthermore, there is no evidence that rivet wheat was ever known in ancient Egypt.

One additional 14-chromosome wheat, *T. timopheevi,* which has no common name, deserves mention. This species was discovered in this century by Russian botanists and is known only in western Georgia, where it is grown on a few thousand acres. The species is of botanical interest because its second set of seven chromosomes, designated genom G, is different from that of any of the other 14-chromosome wheats. It is also of great practical interest because it is resistant to virtually all diseases attacking other cultivated wheats, including rusts, smuts and mildews. In the hands of skilled wheat breeders it may become the ancestor of improved wheats for the next century.

The 21-chromosome wheats, of which there are five, are as a group the most recently evolved and the most useful today. All are cultivated; none has ever been known in the wild. All are products of the hybridization of 14-chromosome wheats containing the genoms A and B with a wild 7-chromosome relative of wheat (almost certainly a grass species of the genus *Aegilops*) containing the genom D. All are believed to have arisen from such hybridization after man, spreading the revolutionary art of agriculture, exposed his earlier cultivated wheats to hybridization with native grasses.

Two of the 21-chromosome wheats, *T. spelta* (spelt) and *T. macha,* are, like einkorn and emmer, hard-threshing species. *T. macha,* like *T. timopheevi,* is confined to western Georgia, where it is grown on not more than a few thousand acres. Spelt was once the principal wheat of central Europe. No archaeological remains of it have been found in the Near East or any part of Asia. There is no doubt about the hybrid origin of spelt, for it has now been synthesized by McFadden and Sears and independently by

H. Kihara in Japan. In both cases the researchers concluded that the botanical characteristics to be sought in the unknown 7-chromosome parent of spelt were possessed by *Aegilops squarrosa*, a completely useless wild grass which grows as a weed in wheat fields from the Balkans to Afghanistan. Both researchers hybridized this wild grass with wild emmer. McFadden and Sears doubled the chromosome number by treatment with colchicine; Kihara was fortunate in discovering a case of natural doubling. The hybrid was highly fertile and similar in characteristics to cultivated spelt. As a final step in a brilliant piece of inductive reasoning and genetic experimentation, McFadden and Sears crossed their synthesized spelt with natural spelt and obtained fully fertile hybrids. The results leave no doubt that the wild grass used in this experiment is one of the parents of cultivated spelt, and they suggest strongly that the other four 21-chromosome wheats are likewise hybrids in which the genom D has been derived from the same grass or a species close to it.

These experiments suggest that cultivated spelt originated in the region where the species of wild grass and wild emmer overlap. But the primitive hulled form of spelt has not been found there. An alternate possibility is that the wild grass hybridized not with wild emmer but with the cultivated species, which has had a much wider distribution. Vavilov concluded that hulled spelt originated in southern Germany. Earlier Elisabeth Schiemann, Germany's leading student of cereals, had placed it in Switzerland and southwest Germany. Both centers are not far from the northeastern limits of the area in which cultivated emmer and the wild grass are known to have occurred together. Thus the botanical and historical evidence are not far apart in indicating a central European origin.

The remaining three species of 21-chromosome wheats are *T. aestivum* (common), *sphaerococcum* (shot) and *compactum* (club). They are the true bread wheats, accounting for about 90 per cent of all the wheat grown in the world today. The three are closely related and easily intercrossed. Whether they are the product of three different hybridizations between 14-chromosome wheats and wild grasses, or of three diverging lines of descent from a single hybridization, is not known. Club and shot wheat differ from common wheat in a number of details whose inheritance is governed by a relatively small number of genes. It is possible, therefore, that the three species are descended from a single hybrid ancestor. Common wheat or something very like it has recently been produced by Kihara by crossing 14-chromosome Persian wheat with the wild grass used to synthesize spelt. Its chromosome number has not yet been doubled, but its botanical characteristics are those of common wheat.

Where and when the modern bread wheat first occurred are still matters for conjecture. Since Persian wheat is known only in a limited area in northeastern Turkey and the adjoining states of the Soviet Union, common wheat very probably originated there. Kernels of shot wheat have been found at the most ancient site in India, Mohenjo-Daro, dated about 2500 B.C. A wheat found in neolithic store-chambers in Hungary has been identified as club wheat. Impressions of grains of bread wheat, either common or club, have been found in the neolithic Dolmen period, dated between 300 and 2300 B.C. The earliest archaeological wheat in Japan, dated in the third century, is regarded by Kihara as a bread wheat. And since the 14-chromosome wheats evidently are recent introductions in China, it is possible that the wheat described in the Chinese classics for the Chou period (about 1000 B.C.) is a 21-chromosome bread wheat. All these items, none in itself conclusive, indicate that the bread wheats originated before the time of Christ but later than einkorn or emmer. A conservative guess would put their origin at approximately 2500 B.C.

LATIN NAME	COMMON NAME	CHROMOSOMES		GROWTH	GRAINS
		NUMBER	GENOMS		
T. AEGILOPOIDES	WILD EINKORN	7	A	WILD	HULLED
T. MONOCOCCUM	EINKORN	7	A	CULTIVATED	HULLED
T. DICOCCOIDES	WILD EMMER	14	AB	WILD	HULLED
T. DICOCCUM	EMMER	14	AB	CULTIVATED	HULLED
T. DURUM	MACARONI WHEAT	14	AB	CULTIVATED	NAKED
T. PERSICUM	PERSIAN WHEAT	14	AB	CULTIVATED	NAKED
T. TURGIDUM	RIVET WHEAT	14	AB	CULTIVATED	NAKED
T. POLONICUM	POLISH WHEAT	14	AB	CULTIVATED	NAKED
T. TIMOPHEEVI		14	AG	CULTIVATED	HULLED
T. AESTIVUM	COMMON WHEAT	21	ABD	CULTIVATED	NAKED
T. SPHAEROCOCCUM	SHOT WHEAT	21	ABD	CULTIVATED	NAKED
T. COMPACTUM	CLUB WHEAT	21	ABD	CULTIVATED	NAKED
T. SPELTA	SPELT	21	ABD	CULTIVATED	HULLED
T. MACHA	MACHA WHEAT	21	ABD	CULTIVATED	HULLED

GEOGRAPHICAL DISTRIBUTION	EARLIEST
WESTERN IRAN. ASIA MINOR. SOUTHEAST EUROPE	PRE-AGRICULTURAL
EASTERN CAUCASUS, ASIA MINOR. CENTRAL EUROPE	4750 B.C.
WESTERN IRAN. ASIA MINOR.	PRE-AGRICULTURAL
INDIA, CENTRAL ASIA, ASIA MINOR. EUROPE,	4000 B.C.
CENTRAL ASIA, ASIA MINOR. SE EUROPE, N AMERICA	100 B.C.
DAGESTAN, GEORGIA, ARMENIA, NORTHEAST TURKEY	NO PREHISTORIC REMAINS
ABYSSINIA, SOUTHERN EUROPE	NO PREHISTORIC REMAINS
ABYSSINIA, MEDITERRANEAN AREA	17TH CENTURY
WESTERN GEORGIA	20TH CENTURY
WORLD WIDE	NEOLITHIC PERIOD
CENTRAL AND NORTHWEST INDIA	2500 B.C.
SOUTHWEST ASIA, SOUTHEAST EUROPE, N AMERICA	NEOLITHIC PERIOD
CENTRAL EUROPE	BRONZE AGE
WESTERN GEORGIA	20TH CENTURY

Characteristics, distribution and antiquity of 14 major wheat strains
are shown in this table. The genoms are sets of inherited characteristics, or combinations of sets. The chromosome number is
a clue to the evolution of wheat. The species with larger chomo-
some numbers are descended from those with small by hybridization and chromosome doubling.

191

Whether the bread wheats originated earlier than this or later, and whether they had one hybrid origin or three, they represent today the most rapid increase in geographical range and numbers of any species of seed-plant in history (see table on page 190). They are now grown in all parts of the world from the Equator to the Arctic Circle. Originating probably not more than 5,000 years ago in the general region of Asia Minor, the new species have increased at an average rate of about 75,000 acres per year until they now occupy almost 400 million acres. Their evolution and dispersal have been explosive phenomena in which man's principal part has been to recognize their usefulness and to open up new agricultural areas for their culture.

The particular value of the bread wheats lies not only in their productiveness and in their free-threshing, naked kernels, but in the peculiar quality of their gluten, the protein component. Of all the cereals only the bread wheats are capable of producing the light, fluffy, leavened breads we know today.

All known species of cultivated wheat, except einkorn and possibly emmer, came into existence spontaneously. Man played no part in their origin except as he spread their culture and their opportunities for natural hybridization over the earth. There is no evidence that ancient man gave much attention to selection of superior forms, or if he did, no evidence that he succeeded. The cultivated einkorn of today is scarcely different from the einkorn of millennia ago, and it, in turn, is no great improvement over wild einkorn. Essentially the same can be said about emmer. Consequently, to speak of primitive man as a plant breeder is to attribute more purposefulness to his activities than the evidence warrants.

Within the past century, especially since the rediscovery of Mendel's laws of inheritance in 1900, vast programs of wheat improvement have been undertaken in almost all the wheat-growing regions of the world. These have been especially successful in the United States and Canada, where a constant succession of new varieties has been introduced. Scarcely any state of the Union today grows extensively the principal varieties of wheat grown 50 years ago.

Early in the century the most common method of wheat breeding was "pure-line" selection as invented by Wilhelm Johannsen, a Danish botanist and geneticist. Johannsen had concluded from experiments on garden beans that self-fertilized plants such as beans, peas and cereals are racial mixtures of many pure lines, differing from one another in many characteristics but each genetically uniform. Continuous selection can have no effect in changing the characters of a genetically pure line, but a mixture of lines can be separated into its component parts and improvements effected by propagating the superior lines.

In practice the wheat breeder selects hundreds of individual heads from a variety, threshes each one separately and grows the progeny of each in a short row called a head row. In succeeding generations more and longer rows are grown, and the pure lines, each originating from a single head, are compared in productiveness and other characteristics. Among wheat breeders in the United States it is standard procedure at this stage to use rows 16 feet long and one foot apart. Rows of this length and spacing simplify computation, since the yield of grain in grams can be converted to a bushel yield per acre by simply pointing off one decimal place. The more promising lines are increased still further in field plots and eventually one is chosen as the best, is named and is distributed to farmers.

The two outstanding United States varieties produced by pure-line selection are both Kansas products. The first, Kanred (Kansas Red), was selected by Herbert Roberts of the Kansas Agricultural Experiment Station from Crimean, a hard, red, winter-type wheat introduced from Russia by Mark Carleton. The first head selections were made in 1906, and the improved pure line first distributed for commercial growing in 1917. By 1925 Kanred wheat, the product of a single head only 19 years earlier, was grown on nearly five million acres in Kansas, Nebraska, Colorado, Oklahoma and Texas. The second Kansas wheat, Blackhull, is the product of a single head selection made in 1912 from a field of Turkey wheat by Earl Clark, a farmer and plant breeder. Blackhull, like Kanred, was first distributed in 1917. By 1929 it occupied almost six million acres, principally in Kansas and Oklahoma.

Pure-line selection merely sorts out from a variety the superior lines already there; it creates no new genetic combinations. To form a new variety the breeder employs hybridization. He selects as parents two varieties with the characteristics he seeks to combine. For example, one parent may be chosen for its superior milling and baking qualities, the other for its resistance to disease. To cross these two the breeder first emasculates one of them by removing the anthers, the male pollen-containing organs, with delicate forceps when these organs are full-grown but not yet ripe. Then he covers the emasculated head with a small glassine bag to prevent uncontrolled pollination. A few days later, when its female organs, the stigmas, have become receptive, the operator pollinates them with ripe anthers taken from the second parent.

Such pollinations produce seeds that grow into first-generation hybrid plants. These are quite uniform and nothing is accomplished by practicing selection among them. But in the second and subsequent generations genetic segregation creates new combinations as numerous and diverse as the hands in a shuffled deck of cards. The opportunities for creative selection are enormous. It is in the early generations following a cross that the plant breeder shows his skill, for at this stage he must select for propagation those combinations which approach most closely the ideal wheat he has in mind and discard those which do not meet his specifications. Eventually genetic segregation produces pure lines.

One of the earliest and greatest achievements in hybrid wheat was the development of the Marquis strain. This variety, a hybrid of early-growing Hard Red Calcutta from India and Red Fife from Poland, was produced in Canada by Charles Saunders, cerealist for the Dominion from 1903 to 1922. The cross from which Marquis wheat was derived had been made in 1892 by his brother Arthur under the direction of his father, William Saunders, who had been hybridizing wheats since 1888. The new hybrid was promising from the beginning. It was a few days earlier than the spring-planted varieties then commonly grown in Canada, thus often avoiding the first frosts. The grain yielded a cream-colored, strongly elastic dough with strong gluten and excellent baking qualities. Marquis wheat later set new standards for baking quality. By 1907, four years after the initial head selection, there were 23 pounds of seed. Distribution to farmers began in the spring of 1909. News of the new wheat spread swiftly from the prairie provinces down into our own spring-wheat belt. By 1913 Marquis seed was being imported into Minnesota and the Dakotas at the rate of 200,000 bushels per year. In 1918 more than 300 million bushels were produced, and the superiority of this variety over those previously grown was a factor in meeting the food shortage of World War I, just as 25 years later hybrid corn was a similar factor in World War II.

For 20 years Marquis was the "king of wheats" in Canada and the United States, and during this period it served as a standard both in the field and in the milling and baking laboratory. Marquis was also used extensively as a parent in new hybrids and is the ancestor of many improved wheats, including Tenmarq, developed in Kansas by John Parker; Ceres, produced in North Dakota by L. R. Waldron, and Thatcher and Newthatch, bred by Herbert K. Hayes and his associates in Minnesota.

Today most new wheat varieties are produced by controlled hybridization rather than by pure-line selection, which is little used. The modern wheat breeder has many objectives. Usually his principal one is productiveness, but involved in this are many factors, including resistance to diseases and tolerance of unfavorable environmental conditions. To test new wheats for these characteristics, breeders have invented devices and methods for subjecting wheat to artificial drought, cold and epidemics of disease.

Breeding for disease resistance is especially important because wheat is a self-fertilized plant which, except for natural hybridization and occasional mutations, tends to remain genetically uniform. A field of wheat of a single variety, especially one originating from a single head, contains millions of plants which are genetically identical. If the variety happens to be susceptible to a disease, it serves as a gigantic culture medium for the propagation of the disease organism, usually a fungus. Thus the growing of new varieties over large acreages increases the hazards from those diseases to which they are susceptible. The result is a never-ending battle between the wheat breeders and the fungi.

The breeding of wheat for resistance to stem rust, a devastating disease, is a prime example. There are many kinds of stem rust. Pathologists, led by Elvin Stakman of the University of Minnesota, have devised ingenious methods of identifying them by inoculation of different hosts. The wheat breeder then develops a new variety which is resistant to the predominating races of stem rust. This is distributed to farmers and its acreage increases rapidly. But while the wheat breeder is hybridizing wheats, nature is hybridizing rusts. The reproductive stage of stem rusts occurs not on wheat but on an alternate host, the common barberry. On this plant new races of rust are constantly created. Although most of them probably die out, one that finds susceptible wheat varieties may multiply prodigiously and in a few years become the predominating race. The wheat breeder then searches the world for wheats resistant to the new hazard and again goes through all the stages of producing a new hybrid variety. The competition between man and the fungi for the wheat crop of the world is a biological contest which never ends.

A wheat breeder must seek not only disease resistance and productiveness but also milling and baking quality. In modern mass-production bakeries with high-speed mixing machinery, dough undergoes stresses and strains which it was never called on to endure when kneaded by hand in the home. As a result wheat breeders have been compelled to subject their new productions to elaborate milling and baking tests which simulate the processes of commercial bakeries. A new wheat that proves superior in the field may be rejected in the laboratory.

In spite of the difficulties involved, the development of more productive varieties of wheat is one of the surest ways of increasing the food supply and raising living standards. When Mussolini drained the Pontine swamp in Italy, the Italian wheat breeder Alzareno Strampelli produced new varieties of wheat which flourished in the fertile soils newly opened to cultivation. An important part of the well-publicized Etawah Village Improvement Program in India is the growing of improved varieties of wheat developed by British and Indian geneticists. Mexico's agricultural program, sponsored by the Rockefeller Foundation in co-operation with the Mexican Government, owes much of its success to new rust-resistant varieties of wheat. Crossing the old varieties of Mexican wheat with rust-resistant wheats from the United States, South America, Australia and New Zealand, the United States breeder Norman Borlaug and his associates, working closely with Mexican technologists, have bred new varieties so resistant to rust that they can be grown in Mexico's summer rainy season as well as in the winter dry season, heretofore its only season for growing wheat. The bulk of Mexico's wheat acreage is now devoted to new hybrids developed since 1943, while acreage and production have expanded substantially.

Hybridization among wheats is usually confined to varieties of one species, but interspecific hybrids also are employed and sometimes are successful. A notable example is the development of Hope wheat by McFadden from a cross of Marquis with Yaroslav emmer, a 14-chromosome wheat extremely resistant to stem rust, leaf rust and several other diseases. From this hybrid, which was partly sterile, McFadden succeeded in developing a 21-chromosome wheat which has a high degree of resistance to many races of stem and leaf rust. Unfortunately Hope wheat has a grain somewhat lacking in milling and baking qualities and the variety has never become important commercially. It has, however, been the parent of many modern varieties of wheat which are commercially grown, including Newthatch in Minnesota, Austin in Texas and several of the new varieties developed in Mexico.

A future possibility in wheat breeding is the creation of wholly new types of cereals by species hybridization followed by artificial chromosome doubling, a man-made counterpart of wheat's earlier evolution in nature. In the U.S.S.R. and the United States wheat has been crossed with rye to produce a fertile, true-breeding hybrid cereal which combines the chromosomes of both. The hybrid, neither a wheat nor a rye, is more resistant to cold than wheat is, but less useful as a bread-making cereal. It has not become popular. Wheat has been crossed with a perennial wild grass to produce a new perennial cereal for which Russian agronomists have made fantastic claims. A field of this wheat, once planted, will, according to the Russians, yield a crop of grain year after year with little or no further attention except to gather the annual harvest. It turns out that this perennial "wheat" may have some promise as a forage grass for livestock, but so far little bread has been made from it and few people have been fed by it.

The idea of producing new cereal species by hybridization and chromosome doubling is, however, quite sound, and the possibilities inherent in it are far from exhausted. Some day new wheat species consciously created by man may replace those which arose spontaneously in nature.

THE MYSTERY OF CORN
by Paul C. Mangelsdorf

THE most important plant in America is corn. It is grown in every state and on three fourths of all the farms of the United States. Corn is the backbone of our agriculture. It is the most efficient plant that we Americans have for trapping the energy of the sun and converting it into food. True, we consume only small amounts of corn directly, but transformed into meat, milk, eggs and other animal products, it is the basic food plant of our civilization.

Yet corn is also a mystery—a botanical mystery as baffling and intriguing as any in the pages of fiction. The plant has become so highly domesticated that it is no longer capable of reproducing itself without man's intervention. A grass, it differs from all other grasses, wild or cultivated, in the nature of its seed-bearing organ: the ear. This is a highly specialized inflorescence, or flower cluster, enclosed in husks, which when mature bears several hundred or more naked seeds upon a rigid cob. The pollen-bearing inflorescence, the tassel, occurs separately on the same plant. The ear of corn has no counterpart anywhere else in the plant kingdom, either in nature or among other cultivated plants. It is superbly constructed for producing grain under man's protection, but it has a low survival value in nature, for it lacks a mechanism of seed dispersal. When an ear of corn drops to the ground, scores of seedlings emerge, creating such fierce competition among themselves for moisture and soil nutrients that usually all die and none reaches the reproductive stage.

What could have been the nature of the wild or primitive corn from which this pampered cereal has developed? Where, when and how was a species, once so hardy that it could survive in the wild, converted to a cultivated plant so specialized and so dependent upon man's ministrations that it would soon become extinct if deprived of man's help? These are questions that have puzzled botanists and anthropologists for more than a century. Now, as a result of research in botany, genetics, archaeology and history, the answers are a little nearer. The mystery has not been solved, but the web of circumstantial evidence is drawing tighter and the final solution is almost in sight.

There is no evidence that corn was known in any part of the Old World in ancient times. Seeds of wheat and barley, and fabrics woven of the fibers of flax and hemp, have been found in ancient Near Eastern sites—but never grains of corn. The Babylonians and Egyptians pictured and described many plants, but nowhere in their art or literature does corn appear. Corn as a plant is not mentioned in the Bible, although some English translations do use the word as a synonym for grain. The Greeks, who had a word for almost everything, had no word for corn. The extensive ancient Chinese literature and the Vedas of India also are completely lacking in any reference to corn. There is no evidence of any kind—archaeological, linguistic, ideographic, pictorial or historical—of the existence of corn in any part of the Old World before 1492.

The first reference to corn in recorded history occurs on November 5, 1492. On that day two Spaniards, whom Christopher Columbus had delegated to explore the interior of Cuba, returned with a report of "a sort of grain they call maiz which was well tasted, bak'd, dry'd and made into flour." Later explorers to the New World found corn being grown by Indians in all parts of America, from Canada to Chile. Corn proved to be as ubiquitous in the New World as it was unknown in the Old. There was a great diversity of corn varieties; all of the principal types we recognize today—dent corn, flint corn, flour corn, sweet corn and popcorn—were already in existence when America was discovered.

Thus the evidence that corn originated in America is so overwhelming that it seems sensible to concentrate, if not to confine, our search for its wild ancestor in the Western Hemisphere. In America corn has obviously had an ancient history. The semi-nomadic hunting and fishing Indians in both North and South America augmented their diet of fish and game with corn from cultivated fields. The more advanced Mound Builders of the Mississippi Valley and the Cliff Dwellers of the Southwest were corn-growing and corn-eating peoples. The highly civilized Mayas of Central America, the warlike and energetic Aztecs of Mexico and the fabulous Incas of Peru and Bolivia all looked to corn for their daily bread. The abundant harvest that corn yielded gave these ancient peoples leisure for weaving beautiful fabrics, for molding exquisite pottery, for building magnificent highways and towering pyramids, for inventing a system of arithmetic and for perfecting a calendar more accurate than the Old World calendar of the same period. Corn was indeed "the grain that built a hemisphere."

This universal reliance of the pre-Columbian cultures on corn as the basic food plant, and its great diversity of varieties, greater than that of any other cereal, bespeak a long period of domestication. How old is corn as a cultivated plant? Fortunately this investigation is no longer wholly a matter of guesswork. Reasonably reliable estimates can be obtained by the ingenious method devised by Willard F. Libby, of the University of Chicago, for determining the age of ancient vegetal remains. The method is to measure the radioactive carbon in the remains; from this one can then determine how much of the radiocarbon originally taken by the plant from the atmosphere has disappeared, and the amount of radioactive decay is a measure of the age of the remains. Libby's determinations of radiocarbon in archaeological remains of corn (not yet published but communicated to the author) tend to bear out previous archaeological and geological estimates that the oldest corn yet found in South America goes back to about 1000 B.C., and the oldest in North America to not earlier than 2000 B.C. The oldest prehistoric ears in both North and South America are small and primitive; they differ decidedly in several characteristics from the modern varieties of the Corn Belt. Yet almost any American farm boy would recognize them instantly as corn. So some 4,000 years ago corn was already well on the road to becoming the unique cereal it is now.

In what part of America did corn originate? And what kind of wild grass was it that gave rise to the multitude of present-day varieties of corn?

One theory has corn originating from a plant called by the Aztecs *teocintle* (now Anglicized to teosinte). Teosinte is undoubtedly the closest wild relative of cultivated corn. Like corn, it has tassels and ears borne separately, although its "ears" contain only five or six seeds, each enclosed in a hard bony shell —characteristics that make teosinte a most unpromising food plant. Also like corn, it has 10 chromosomes, indicating that it is a closely related species. Teosinte can readily be crossed with corn to produce hybrids that are completely fertile or almost so. If corn came from teosinte, as many botanists have supposed, it must have originated in Guatemala or Mexico, for teosinte is found only in these two areas.

The second principal theory is that corn originated in South America from a peculiar primitive plant called "pod" corn. Primitive pod corn today has virtually vanished; it is no longer found in pure form but as an admixture in modern varieties. As described in early references, and as obtained by inbreeding from present-day mixtures, pod corn has its kernels enclosed in a pod or chaffy shell similar to that found in all other cereals—a condition which almost certainly was characteristic of wild corn.

Which, if either, of these two theories is more likely to be correct? Botanists, in attempting to determine the place of origin of a cultivated plant, place considerable reliance upon two criteria. One is the occurrence of wild relatives of the plant in question; the other is diversity in the cultivated species itself. It is assumed that, other things being equal, the region of maximum diversity should coincide with the center of origin, since diversification has progressed longer at the center than at the periphery of the plant's present range. In the case of corn the two clues point in opposite directions: the wild-relative clue points to Guatemala and Mexico, where teosinte, corn's closest relative, grows; the diversity clue points to South America, where, on the eastern slopes of the Andes, occurs the greatest diversity of corn varieties found anywhere in America in a region of comparable size.

Some 20 years ago my colleague Robert G. Reeves and I began working at the Agricultural Experiment Station of Texas A. & M. College on a series of genetic and cytological studies of corn and its relatives to test these two conflicting theories. We hybridized corn with teosinte to determine how the genes that differentiate the two species are inherited and how they are distributed on the chromosomes. We also hybridized corn with Tripsacum, a more distant wild relative of corn, which occurs in both North and South America. Our hybrids of corn and teosinte revealed that corn differs from teosinte not by a relatively few genes, as might be expected if the one had been derived from the other as a result of domestication, but by a large number of genes inherited in blocks. Our hybrids of corn and Tripsacum, the first such hybrids ever to be made, showed that the chromosomes of Tripsacum, 18 in number, differed greatly from those of corn. Microscopic studies of the reproductive cells of the Tripsacum-corn hybrids showed little pairing (a criterion of relationship) between the chromosomes of the two species. Nevertheless, there was some chromosome association and consequently some opportunity for exchange of genes. Especially important was the discovery that some of the plants that occurred in later generations of the Tripsacum-corn hybrid resembled teosinte in some of their characteristics. This discovery led to the conclusion that teosinte might well be not the ancestor but a descendant of corn—the product of the natural hybridization of corn and Tripsacum. Such a possibility had been suggested years earlier by Edgar Anderson of the Missouri Botanical Garden.

Since 1937, when we arrived at this working hypothesis, much additional research has been done on corn, pod corn, teosinte and Tripsacum, and upon their hybrids. There is abundant circumstantial evidence, but still no conclusive proof, that teosinte is the product of the hybridization of corn and Tripsacum. There is even more evidence to show that teosinte could scarcely have been corn's ancestor. Reeves, who has made an intensive study of the botanical characteristics of corn, teosinte and Tripsacum, has found that teosinte is intermediate between corn and Tripsacum or is identical with one or the other of these two species in the 50 or more features in which they differ.

John S. Rogers, also working at the Texas Experiment Station, has hybridized corn with five different varieties of teosinte obtained from various parts of Mexico and Guatemala. He has found that numerous genes, many more than previously supposed, are involved in differentiating teosinte from corn. One of the Guatemalan teosintes, for example, differs from corn in certain ear characteristics controlled by genes borne on two chromosomes. It differs in its photoperiodic response through differing genes on three other chromosomes. (In contrast to corn, teosinte is a "short-day" plant, blooming only in seasons when the days are appreciably shorter than the nights.) It differs in the number of tillers, or "suckers," in genes on four chromosomes, one of which is also involved in the ear characteristics. Altogether eight different chromosomes and possibly numerous genes on each are involved in just these three of the many differences between corn and teosinte. The possibility that these considerable genetic differences could have originated during a few thousand years of domestication seems remote indeed.

So the teosinte theory has become increasingly untenable. Meanwhile the theory that corn originated from pod corn has become more and more plausible. When a modern hybrid form of pod corn is inbred (a process that usually intensifies inherent traits) the result is a plant quite different from ordinary cultivated corn. The ear disappears and the kernels, now borne on the branches of the tassel, are enclosed in glumes, or chaff, as in other cereals. This pure pod corn possesses a means of dispersal, since its seeds are not on a heavy ear but on fragile branches. In the proper environment it could undoubtedly survive in the wild and reproduce itself. It has characteristics like those of many wild grasses; indeed, in its principal botanical features it is quite similar to its wild relative Tripsacum. Pure pod corn has virtually all of the characteristics we would expect to find in the ancestral form of corn. Furthermore, it is more than a relative of corn; it *is* corn —a form of corn that differs from cultivated corn in exactly the way a wild species ought to differ from its cultivated counterpart. Finally, all the hereditary differences between pod corn and cultivated corn are traceable to just one gene on one chromosome. Thus a single mutation can change pod corn to the nonpodded form, and it has actually done so in my cultures.

The aboriginal wild corn that man began to cultivate undoubtedly had other primitive characteristics in addition to those of the ancestral pod corn. Its kernels, for example, were probably small, hard and pointed. Kernels of this kind are found today in varieties of popcorn. Indeed, the United States botanist E. Lewis Sturtevant, one of corn's most astute investigators, concluded more than half a century ago that primitive corn must have been both a pod corn and a popcorn. Evidence is now accumulating to show that Sturtevant was right.

In the remains of prehistoric civilizations unearthed in South America, popcorn predominates over other types. Pottery utensils for popping corn, as well as actual specimens of the popped grains, have been found in prehistoric Peruvian graves. Certainly there is nothing new about the popcorn which modern Americans consume so lavishly as part of the movie-going ritual. Popcorn is an ancient food, and it is quite possible that primitive man first discovered the usefulness of corn as a food plant when a wild corn was accidentally exposed to heat. This would have exploded the small, vitreous, glume-covered kernels, and transformed what to people with no grinding tools other than their own teeth was a very unpromising food into tender, tasty, nutritious morsels.

There is an interesting historical reference which lends support to Sturtevant's conclusion that primitive corn was both a pod corn and a popcorn. A century and a half ago Félix de Azara, the Spanish Commissioner to Paraguay, wrote of a peculiar variety of corn in Paraguay in which small seeds enclosed in "envelopes" were borne in the tassel. When the tassels were heated in hot oil, the kernels exploded to produce "a superb bouquet capable of adorning at night the head of a lady."

By a very simple experiment in our breeding plots, we have succeeded in duplicating exactly the corn Azara described. Pod corn was hybridized with popcorn and was then inbred to produce an earless plant bearing in the branches of the tassel small hard seeds enclosed in glumes. When a tassel of this pod-popcorn

207

was heated in hot oil, it behaved exactly like the corn of Azara. The kernels exploded but remained attached to the tassel to produce the "bouquet" he described.

These recent findings have quite naturally given new impetus to the search for wild corn in South America, since the most convincing and conclusive proof of the pod-corn theory would be the discovery of a primitive pod corn still existing in the wild state. The search for a wild corn has not so far been successful in its primary objective, but it has been quite fruitful in turning up new types of corn, especially less extreme forms of pod corn whose kernels are only partially enclosed in glumes. Perhaps wild corn will still be discovered in some remote protected spot in a region not yet thoroughly explored. The odds are at least even, however, that it no longer exists. Corn in the wild may well have been a plant with low survival value, restricted in its range, and already well on the road to eventual extinction when first used by man.

In the meantime a wholly unexpected discovery, made within the past two years, has furnished direct evidence for the theory that primitive corn was both a pod corn and a popcorn. During the summer of 1948 an expedition sponsored by the Peabody Museum of Harvard University and led by Herbert W. Dick, a graduate student in anthropology, uncovered many cobs and other parts of corn from the accumulated refuse in an abandoned rock shelter in New Mexico known as Bat Cave. This shelter was occupied from about 2000 B.C. to A.D. 1000. Uninhibited by modern concepts of sanitation, its successive generations of occupants allowed refuse and trash to accumulate in the cave to a depth of about six feet. Carefully removed and sifted by the archaeologists, the refuse yielded 766 specimens of shelled cobs, 125 loose kernels and various fragments of husks, leaf sheaths and tassels. The cobs are of particular interest, since they reveal a distinct evolutionary sequence. The oldest, at the bottom of the refuse heap, are the smallest and most primitive. These cobs and loose kernels from the same level prove that the earliest Bat Cave people grew a primitive variety of corn which was both a popcorn and a form of pod corn. The pod corn, however, was not as extreme as the earless synthetic "wild" corn described above. It probably represents a type already partly modified by domestication, more nearly like the weak forms of pod corn still found in South American varieties.

The Bat Cave corn has answered another of our questions: What is the relationship of corn to teosinte? The oldest and most primitive of the Bat Cave corn shows no evidence whatever of having stemmed from teosinte. But beginning about midway in the sequence there is strong evidence of the introduction of a corn that had become contaminated with teosinte. Thus the Bat Cave cobs suggest that early botanical investigators were not completely wrong in believing that teosinte played a role in the evolution of corn. Although teosinte clearly was not the progenitor of corn, it contributed its genes to corn's progress toward its present form.

The Bat Cave remains still leave unanswered the question: Where in America did corn originate? It seems improbable that corn could have been a native of the region where these remains were found, since corn is a moisture-loving plant and the region is now and was then quite dry. Probably it was brought into the Bat Cave region as a cultivated plant from Mexico. Whether corn was native to Mexico or had been introduced there still earlier from South America is an open question.

How did the primitive pod-popcorn that the Bat Cave people grew 4,000 years ago evolve in so short a period, as evolutionary time is measured, into the modern ear of the Corn Belt? Some botanists are inclined to endow the American Indian with unusual abilities as a plant breeder. If the great changes that have occurred in corn in this relatively brief period are the product of his skill, he was indeed remarkably adroit. The corn from Bat Cave does not, however, support this view. On the contrary, there is no evidence that the Bat Cave people were any more concerned with plant improvement than they were with sanitation. If selection was practiced at all, it was probably an unplanned "negative" selection—the good ears were consumed and the leftover nubbins were used for seed. Nevertheless, thanks probably to accidental hybridization with teosinte and with other races of corn, there was a gradual increase in the average size of ears and kernels and an enormous increase in total variation during the 3,000 years of the Bat Cave's history.

The evolutionary sequence in the Bat Cave indicates that four principal factors operated in the evolution of corn during this period: (1) The pressure of natural selection, one of the most important suppressive factors in evolution, was greatly reduced; (2) mutations from the more to the less extreme forms of pod corn occurred; (3) corn was modified by contamination with teosinte; (4) crossing of varieties and races produced new combinations of characters and a high degree of hybridity.

All of these factors contributed to a tremendous increase in variation, so that when man finally did begin to practice selection in corn, he had a rich diversity at his disposal. From this, by accident or design, he chose a combination of characteristics that makes corn the most efficient of all cereals as a producer of foodstuffs. The ear of modern Corn Belt corn is a highly functional botanical structure. The massive cob provides an extensive surface for grain-bearing. It encloses an enormous system of vessels which supply and nourish the grains. The entire ear, once an aggregate of kernels individually enclosed in glumes, is now protected as a single unit by the husks. The glumes have been reduced to mere vestiges—no energy is wasted on structures now useless and obsolete. The elements of strength necessary to support this greatly enlarged inflorescence have come from teosinte, which contributes genes for hardness and toughness when it is hybridized with corn. Teosinte is to the modern ear of corn what steel is to the modern skyscraper. Indeed, in structure the skyscraper and the ear of corn are not too unlike. Both are massive, strong, efficient, functional and superbly designed to fit a particular purpose. At their best both are distinctly beautiful.

HYBRID CORN

by Paul C. Mangelsdorf

Hᴙʙʀɪᴅ ᴄᴏʀɴ, a man-made product developed during the past 25 years, may prove to be the most far-reaching contribution in applied biology of this century. With its accompanying improvements in farming methods, it has revolutionized the agriculture of the American Corn Belt. Because of it United States farmers are growing more corn on fewer acres than ever before in this country's history. The new abundance of food brought by hybrid corn played a significant role in World War II and in the rehabilitation of Europe after the war. Now this product, spreading throughout the Americas, to Europe and, under state-planned forced draught, into the agricultural economy of the U.S.S.R., promises to become a factor of considerable consequence in solving the world food problem.

What is hybrid corn and how has it made possible these substantial contributions to the world's food resources?

In a broad sense all corn is hybrid, for this plant is a cross-pollinated species in which hybridization between individual plants, between varieties and between races occurs constantly. Such natural, more or less accidental hybridization has played a major role in corn's evolution under domestication, as I have explained in the preceding chapter. But the hybrid corn with which we shall deal here is a planned exploitation of this natural tendency on a scale far beyond that possible in nature.

The biological basis of hybrid corn is a genetic phenomenon known as "hybrid vigor." It means simply that crossed animals or plants have greater vigor or capacity for growth than those produced by inbreeding. This fact has been known since Biblical times. The ancient Near Eastern peoples who mated the horse and the ass to produce a sterile hybrid, the mule, were creating and utilizing hybrid vigor. The mule is an excellent example of the practical advantages that often follow crossing. This animal, said to be "without pride of ancestry or hope of posterity," has greater endurance than either of its parents; it is usually longer-lived than the horse, less subject to diseases and injury and more efficient in the use of food. Hybrid corn resembles the mule (indeed, it used to be called "mule corn") in being more useful to man than either of its parents.

The idea of crossing varieties of corn is as old as some of the early American Indian tribes, who regularly planted different kinds of corn close together to promote hybridization and increase yields. Cotton Mather, of witch-hunting fame, published in 1716 observations on the natural crossing of corn varieties, and James Logan, onetime Governor of Pennsylvania, in 1735 conducted experiments which demonstrated natural crossing between corn plants.

But it was Charles Darwin who made the important studies of hybrid vigor in plants which open the story of modern hybrid corn. He investigated the effects of self-pollination and cross-pollination in plants, including corn as one of his subjects. His were the first controlled experiments in which crossed and self-bred individuals were compared under identical environmental conditions. He was the first to see that it was the crossing between unrelated varieties of a plant, not the mere act of crossing itself, that produced hybrid vigor, for he found that when separate flowers on the same plant or different plants of the same strain were crossed, their progeny did not possess such vigor. He concluded, quite correctly, that the phenomenon occurred only when diverse heredities were united. These researches, together

213

with his theory of evolution, inspired the studies on heredity which eventually led to the discovery of the principles underlying the production of hybrid corn.

Darwin's experiments were known, even before their publication, to the American botanist Asa Gray, with whom Darwin was in more or less constant communication. One of Gray's students, William Beal, became, like Gray, an admirer and follower of Darwin. At Michigan State College Beal undertook the first controlled experiments aimed at the improvement of corn through the utilization of hybrid vigor. He selected some of the varieties of flint and dent corn then commonly grown and planted them together in a field isolated from other corn. He removed the tassels—the pollen-bearing male flower clusters—from one variety before the pollen was shed. The female flowers of these emasculated plants then had to receive their pollen from the tassels of another variety. The seed borne on the detasseled plants, being a crossed breed, produced only hybrid plants when planted the following season.

The technique Beal invented for crossing corn—planting two kinds in the same field and removing the tassels of one—proved highly successful and is still essentially the method employed today in producing hybrid seed corn. But as a device for increasing corn yield his operation of crossing two unselected varieties, each of mixed inheritance, was ineffective: the gain in yield was seldom large enough to justify the time and care spent in crossing the plants. The missing requirement—the basic principle that made hybrid corn practicable—was discovered by George H. Shull of the Carnegie Institution.

His discovery was an unexpected by-product of theoretical studies on inheritance which he had begun in 1905. Shull's contribution grew from certain earlier studies made by two great scientists: Darwin's cousin Francis Galton and the Danish botanist Wilhelm Ludwig Johannsen. Galton had recognized that

214

the result of the combination of parental heredity could take two forms: an "alternative" inheritance, such as the coat color of basset hounds, which came from one parent or the other but was not a mixture of both, and a "blended" inheritance, such as in human stature. He observed that children of very tall parents are shorter than their parents, on the average, while children of very short parents tend to be taller. These observations led Galton to the formulation of his "law of regression," which holds that the progeny of parents above or below the average in any given characteristic tend to regress toward the average.

This regression is seldom complete, however, and Johannsen saw in that circumstance an opportunity for controlling heredity through the selection in successive generations of extreme variations. He tested the possibility by trying to breed unusually large and unusually small beans by selection. He found that, although selection apparently was effective in the first generation, it had no measurable effect whatever in later generations. Johannsen concluded that in self-fertilized plants such as the bean the progeny of a single plant represent a "pure line" in which all individuals are genetically identical and in which any residual variation is environmental in origin. He postulated that an unselected race such as the ordinary garden bean with which he started his experiments was a mixture of pure lines differing among themselves in many characteristics but each one genetically uniform. Johannsen's pure-line theory has been widely applied to the improvement of cereals and other self-fertilized plants. Many of the varieties of wheat, oats, barley, rice, sorghum and flax grown today are the result of sorting out the pure lines in mixed agricultural races and identifying and multiplying the superior ones.

Shull's contribution was to apply the pure-line theory to corn, with spectacular, though unpremeditated, results. He started with the objective of analyzing the inheritance of quantitative or "blending" characteristics, and he chose the number of rows of

215

kernels in an ear of corn as an inherited quantitative characteristic suitable for study. Through self-pollination he developed a number of inbred lines of corn with various numbers of rows of kernels. These lines, as a consequence of inbreeding, declined in vigor and productiveness, and at the same time each became quite uniform. Shull concluded correctly that he had isolated pure lines of corn similar to those in beans described by Johannsen. Then, as the first step in studying the inheritance of kernel-row number, he crossed these pure lines. The results were surprising and highly significant. The hybrids between two pure lines were quite uniform, like their inbred parents, but unlike their parents they were vigorous and productive. Some were definitely superior to the original open-pollinated variety from which they had been derived. Inbreeding had isolated, from a single heterogeneous species, the diverse germinal entities whose union Darwin had earlier postulated as the cause of hybrid vigor.

Shull recognized at once that inbreeding followed by crossing offered an entirely new method of improving the yield of corn. In two papers published in 1908 and 1909 he reported his results and outlined a method of corn breeding based upon his discoveries. He proposed the isolation of inbred strains as a first step and the crossing of two such inbred strains as a second. Only the first-generation cross was to be used for seed for crop production, because hybrid vigor is always at its maximum in the first generation. Shull's idea of growing otherwise useless inbred strains of corn solely for later crossing was revolutionary as a method of corn breeding, but it eventually won acceptance and is now the basis that underlies almost the entire hybrid seed-corn enterprise.

However, Shull's suggestion for the second step—the crossing of two weak inbred strains, known as a single cross—proved impractical as a method of seed production. Because the inbred strains are relatively unproductive, hybrid seed obtained in this way is too expensive except for certain special purposes.

One further major development was needed to make hybrid corn practicable and the great boon to agriculture that it has become. This contribution came from the Connecticut Agricultural Experiment Station by the end of the second decade of this century. The story begins in 1906, when Edward M. East arrived there from the University of Illinois, where he had participated in corn-breeding experiments with some of Beal's former students. At the Connecticut Station, East began a series of studies of the effects of corn inbreeding and crossbreeding which were to continue to this day and yield a great deal of information about corn, including the effects of selection on its chemistry. It was East who called attention to the need for developing a more practical method for producing hybrid seed. It remained for Donald Jones, one of East's students, who assumed charge of the Connecticut experiments in 1915, to invent a method which solved the problem.

Jones's solution was simply to use seed from a double cross instead of a single cross. The double cross, which combines four inbred strains, is a hybrid of two single crosses. For example, two inbred strains, A and B, are combined to produce the single cross A × B. Two additional inbred strains, C and D, are combined to produce a second single cross C × D. All four strains are now brought together in the double cross (A × B) × (C × D) (see diagram on page 219). At first glance it may seem paradoxical to solve the problem of hybrid seed production by making three crosses instead of one. But the double cross is actually an ingenious device for making a small amount of scarce single-crossed seed go a long way. Whereas single-crossed seed is produced from undersized ears borne on stunted inbred plants, double-crossed seed is produced on normal-sized ears borne on vigorous single-cross plants. A few bushels of single-crossed seed can be converted in one generation to several thousand bushels of double-crossed seed. The difference in cost of the two kinds of seed is reflected in the units in which they are sold: double-crossed seed is priced by the bushel, single-crossed seed by the thousand seeds. Double-cross hybrids are never as uniform as single crosses, but they may be just as productive or more so.

Jones made a second important contribution to the development of hybrid corn by presenting a genetic interpretation of hybrid vigor. Shull and East had suggested that hybrid vigor was due to some physiological stimulation resulting from hybridity itself. Shull was quite certain that something more than gene action was involved. He thought that part of the stimulation might be derived from the interaction between the male nucleus and the egg cytoplasm. Jones proposed the theory that hybrid vigor is the product of bringing together in the hybrid the favorable genes of both parents. These are usually partly dominant. Thus if one inbred strain has the genes *AA BB cc dd* (to use a greatly oversimplified example), and the other has the genes *aa bb CC DD*, the first-generation hybrid has the genetic constitution, *Aa Bb Cc Dd*. Since the genes *A, B, C* and *D* are assumed not only to have favorable effects but to be partially dominant in their action, the hybrid contains the best genes of both parents and is correspondingly better than either parent. Jones's theory differs from a similar earlier theory in assuming that the genes involved are so numerous that several are borne on the same chromosome and thus tend to be inherited in groups. This explains why vigor is at its maximum in the first generation after crossing,

Hybrid corn is the product of the double crossing of strains shown here. First two pairs of inbred corn plants are crossed *(top)*; then the process is repeated with their hybrid descendants *(bottom)*. The second cross greatly multiplies the number of seeds produced by the first.

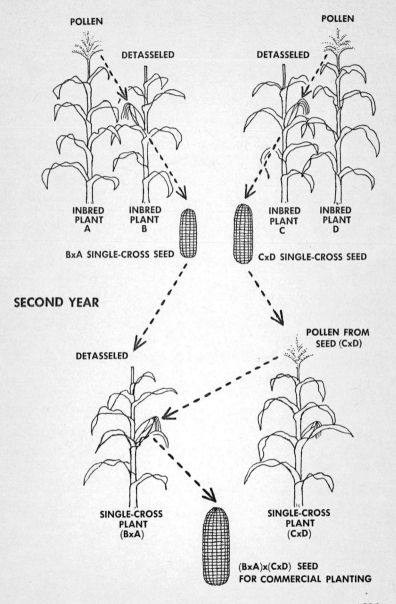

FIRST YEAR

POLLEN

DETASSELED

DETASSELED

POLLEN

INBRED PLANT A

INBRED PLANT B

INBRED PLANT C

INBRED PLANT D

BxA SINGLE-CROSS SEED

CxD SINGLE-CROSS SEED

SECOND YEAR

POLLEN FROM SEED (CxD)

DETASSELED

SINGLE-CROSS PLANT (BxA)

SINGLE-CROSS PLANT (CxD)

(BxA)x(CxD) SEED FOR COMMERCIAL PLANTING

219

and why it is impossible through selection in later generations to incorporate all of the favorable genes into a new variety as good as or better than the first-generation hybrid. The ideal combination *AA BB CC DD*, which combines all of the favorable genes, is impossible to attain because of chromosomal linkage. For example, the genes *B* and *c* may be borne at adjacent loci on the same chromosome and thus be inseparably joined in their inheritance. Although Jones's theory is not universally accepted, and it now seems probable that hybrid vigor involves still other genetic mechanisms, it nevertheless gave great stimulus to practical hybrid corn breeding.

Historically, then, hybrid corn was transformed from Shull's magnificent design to the practical reality it now is when Jones's method of seed production made it feasible and his theory of hybrid vigor made it plausible. This combination proved irresistible to even the most conservative agronomists. Soon after 1917 hybrid corn-breeding programs were initiated in many states. By 1933 hybrid corn was in commercial production on a substantial scale, and the United States Department of Agriculture had begun to gather statistics on it. By 1950 more than three fourths of the total corn acreage of the United States, some 65 million acres, was in hybrid corn.

This immense achievement stems from the work of many corn breeders, variously associated with the United States Department of Agriculture, state experiment stations and private industry. Among the pioneers in the breeding of corn were Henry A. Wallace, Herbert K. Hayes and Frederick D. Richey.

Hybrid corn is usually produced now by a process that involves three principal steps. To understand them we must consider briefly how corn produces progeny. The corn plant is unique among the major cereals in bearing its male and female flower clusters separately on the same plant. One cluster, the ear, bears only female flowers—several hundred or more enclosed in husks, each with its silk to receive the male pollen. The other, the tassel, bears only male flowers, usually more than a thousand in number. Each male flower contains three anthers, or pollen sacs, and each anther contains about 2,500 pollen grains. A single corn plant sheds several million pollen grains during its flowering period. These are so small and light and so easily carried by the wind that they seldom fall upon the silks of the same plant. As a consequence, under natural conditions cross-pollination is the rule. In experimental or seed-production plots special arrangements are made to control pollination. Experimental pollinations are usually made under bags. The young ears bearing the female flowers are covered with glassine or parchment bags before the silks have appeared. At the same time or a few days later the tassels also are bagged, for the collection of pollen. A single pollination produces an ear bearing several hundred seeds. A single bagged tassel produces enough pollen to pollinate several hundred ears.

The first step in the production of hybrid corn is the isolation of inbred strains. This is still accomplished, as in Shull's and East's experiments, by self-pollination. Hundreds of thousands of self-pollinations in corn are made each year, and tons of paper bags are consumed in the process. The manufacture of special corn-pollinating bags has become a recognized minor industry.

Self-pollination is a form of inbreeding approximately three times as intensive in its effects as matings between brothers and sisters in animals. The same plant is literally both the father and the mother of the offspring. Some plants—wheat, rice, barley and oats, for example—are naturally self-pollinated and suffer no deleterious effects from the process. But corn, a naturally cross-pollinated plant, responds to inbreeding with conspicuous effects. First, in the early generations many inherited abnormalities appear—defective seeds, dwarfs, albinos, stripes and a host of other chlorophyll deficiencies. These abnormalities were once supposed to be the degenerative products of the "unnatural" process of inbreeding, but it is now known that inbreeding merely brings to light deleterious characters already present, which have previously remained hidden because they are recessive traits. Inbreeding actually helps the corn breeder, for it reveals hidden defects and allows the breeder to remove them permanently from his stocks.

After five or six generations of inbreeding the inbred strains have become remarkably uniform, much more uniform than any variety of corn occurring naturally. All the plants of a single strain are genetically identical, or almost so; and their genetic uniformity is reflected in a remarkable uniformity in all perceptible characteristics, physical and physiological. But even the best of these uniform strains yield no more than half as much as the open-pollinated varieties from which they were derived, and many yield much less. Their only value is as potential parents of productive hybrids.

Inbreeding accompanied by selection has given the corn breeder a remarkable degree of control over corn's heredity. Much of the breeding work today is aimed not only at greater yields but also at improvements in other characteristics. Almost all the corn now grown in the Corn Belt has been bred to possess stiff stalks that remain upright far into the fall—an important quality for mechanical harvesting. Some breeders, shaping the corn to the machines, are developing hybrids bearing two or three small ears instead of a single large one. Resistance to drought was recognized as an important characteristic during the hot dry summers of the 1930s and has been incorporated into many hybrids. Hybrid corn has also been bred for resistance to various diseases. Through selection corn varieties can even be developed to withstand the depredations of insects. Some inbred strains of corn are quite resistant to chinch-bug injury. Others are either unattractive to root worms or survive their assaults. The Southern corn breeder uses corn with long tight husks, which protect the ears against the inroads of ear worms and weevils. Corn breeders in Argentina claim to have isolated lines that contain a bitter substance rendering the foliage unattractive to grasshoppers. This same corn has been used in the United States in an attempt to develop new strains possibly resistant to the European corn borer. Strains resistant to corn-borer damage are frequently also unpalatable to aphids.

After inbreeding, the second step in the production of hybrid corn is the testing of the inbred lines in various crossing combinations to determine their hybrid performance. Usually the lines are first screened by crossing all to a common parent—an open-pollinated variety. This comparison allows the corn breeder to eliminate many of the poorer strains. The more promising ones are then tested further in single or double crosses. Of each hundred lines isolated, usually not more than one or two prove satisfactory for use in hybrids.

The final step in producing hybrid seed is to combine the selected strains into commercial hybrids. In sweet corn, especially for canning, where uniformity in the size and shape of the ears is a more important consideration than the cost of the seed, the product is usually a single cross. In field corn the cost of the seed is paramount, so all the seed produced for use is double-crossed. A given amount of land and labor will yield two to three times as much double-crossed seed as single-crossed.

Because the second-generation progeny of a hybrid decline markedly in yield and because uniformity disappears, only one crop of corn is grown from the crossed seed. Hence the farmer must buy new hybrid seed each season. The production of hybrid seed corn has become a huge and highly specialized enterprise comparable to the pharmaceutical industry. Hundreds of different hybrids, adapted to a wide variety of soils and climates, are produced. Like vaccines and serums, they cannot be identified by their appearance. It is their inherent genetic qualities that distinguish hybrids from one another, and farmers have learned to buy hybrid seed on the basis of these qualities.

The almost universal use of hybrid corn in the United States, and the prospective wide adoption of it in other parts of the world, is not without its dangers. Chief among these is that farmers as a rule are no longer growing the open-pollinated varieties. These varieties, from which all inbred strains are ultimately derived, may therefore become extinct. Already more than 99 per cent of the corn acreage in several of the Corn Belt states is in hybrid corn; in Iowa it is 100 per cent hybrid. The loss of the original source of breeding material would mean not only that improvement of the present strains would be restricted but that new types of hybrid corn could not be developed to cope with new diseases or insect pests suddenly become rampant. Our corn would also lose the ability to adapt to climatic changes. Open-pollinated varieties of corn, in which cross-pollination is the rule, are admirably contrived for maintaining genetic plasticity and would be capable of surviving rather drastic changes in the environment. Hybrid corn, a small, highly selected sample of the original genetic diversity, has lost this capability.

The United States Department of Agriculture, recognizing the danger, has taken steps to maintain the open-pollinated varieties of the Corn Belt. It is also important, however, to preserve the indigenous corn varieties of other parts of the United States and of the countries of Latin America. Many of the United States varieties had their origin in Mexico, and Mexican corn in turn has ancient affinities with the corn of Central and South America. The indigenous varieties of the countries to our south may one day become of critical importance as sources of new genes to improve, or perhaps even to save, the corn of the United States. The National Research Council is therefore planning, in co-operation with the Department of Agriculture, the State Department and other agencies, to collect and preserve the native corn varieties in the principal corn-growing countries of this hemisphere.

What does the future hold for hybrid corn? To a large extent this will hinge on basic research in corn genetics. Unfortunately, new discoveries have not kept pace with practical utilization. Corn breeders, like applied scientists in other fields, have been spending the accumulated capital of theoretical research of the past without taking adequate steps to create new capital. Still unsolved, for example, is the problem of the genetic basis of hybrid vigor, which is clearly of more than academic interest to the practical corn breeder.

Some advances can still be made by the application of present knowledge. Already a trend has begun toward developing highly specialized types of corn for particular purposes. There are special white corn varieties (lacking the pigment carotene) which are used for the manufacture of hominy; a "waxy" corn containing large amounts of the carbohydrate amylopectin has been developed for industrial purposes, including the making of tapioca; for feeding meat-animals breeders have produced a corn with a high protein content. It is possible that corn may be bred with a higher content of the pellagra-preventing vitamins of the B complex, especially niacin, in which corn is now notoriously deficient.

The methods of production no doubt also will be improved. Two techniques for creating uniform strains without prolonged inbreeding are under trial. One is now being tested by Sherret Chase at Iowa State College. This method involves the use of "haploid" plants, which contain only half of the normal number of chromosomes. Such plants occur spontaneously. Haploid plants are weak, often sterile and of no value in themselves. But their chromosomes can be doubled by treatment with the alkaloid colchicine, or they may double spontaneously. When this happens, they produce offspring containing the normal number of chromosomes. Since all the chromosomes come from a single original parental germ cell, plants derived in this way are completely pure for all of their genes and are even more uniform than strains resulting from inbreeding.

A second short-cut method for obtaining uniform strains has been suggested by Charles R. Burnham of the University of Minnesota. By treating seed with X rays Burnham is attempting to produce an artificial stock of corn in which the chromosomes are broken and so "scrambled" that they will no longer form normal pairs with the chromosomes in normal plants when hybridized with them. Such hybrids, when self-pollinated, should produce three kinds of plants, of which one should have only normal chromosomes and be pure for all of its genes. Plants of the latter kind would be the equivalent of inbred strains.

The operation of detasseling as a prelude to crossing is also destined to be simplified. Detasseling has been called the "peskiest and most expensive" part of producing hybrid seed corn. Each summer the seed industry must find and train thousands of temporary workers, many of them high-school students, to perform this essential task. One firm alone employs more than 20,000 laborers during the detasseling season, and it has been estimated that on the peak day of the season some 125,000 persons in the United States are engaged in removing tassels from corn plants. Many attempts have been made to simplify this operation or eliminate it entirely, but until recently none was notably successful. Now what promises to be a partial solution to the problem has been discovered. It involves a certain form of sterility in corn which prevents the tassels from shedding pollen but which is transmitted only through the seeds. Marcus Rhoades of the University of Illinois has shown that this kind of sterility is inherited not through the chromosomes but through the cytoplasm of the germ cells. Jones and I have found that it can easily be incorporated into any inbred strain of corn by crossing, and that it is an excellent substitute for detasseling. A sterile inbred crossed to a fertile inbred produces a sterile single cross. A sterile single cross grown in a crossing field requires no detasseling. The resulting double cross also is sterile; that is, it produces no pollen. But it can be pollinated by planting it with a certain proportion of a comparable fertile double cross. Another method of obtaining a crop from it is to prevent the double cross from being sterile by incorporating in it an inbred strain carrying fertility-restoring genes. This scheme, which has proved completely successful in Jones's experimental cultures, is the last word in the biological manipulation of the corn plant. It employs hereditary factors in the cytoplasm to make corn sterile when sterility is a distinct asset, and uses hereditary factors on the chromosomes to make it fertile when fertility is essential. Hybrid seed produced in this way was grown on a commercial scale for the first time in 1951.

Hybrid corn well illustrates the importance of the free interplay of theory and practice. The practical motive of improving corn has played its part, but the development of hybrid corn is due in even greater measure to fundamental research aimed only at increasing theoretical knowledge in genetics. Progress of the kind represented by this development is most likely to occur in a free society where truth is sought for its own sake and where there is no undue emphasis on utilitarian aspects. In the case of hybrid corn, breeders actually had to go back before they went forward: the first step, inbreeding, led not to immediate improvement but to a drastic reduction in yield. To avoid having to defend this paradoxical procedure of "advancing backwards," corn breeders sometimes took the precaution of planting their experimental plots of stunted inbred corn in out-of-the-way places where the public was not likely to see them.

Hybrid corn's greatest significance lies in the contributions which it and similar developments in applied genetics can make to the world food supply. What hybrid corn has already accomplished toward this end is illustrated by two dramatic examples. During three war years, 1942 to 1944, the American farmer, though afflicted with an acute labor shortage and unfavorable weather, produced 90 per cent as much corn as he had during the previous four years of peace, themselves years of unprecedented production. In other words, hybrid corn enabled him to add a 20 per cent increase to the previous gains. Thanks to hybrid corn, the United States suffered no real food shortages at home, was able to ship vast quantities of food abroad to her Allies, and still had enough surplus grain to use large quantities in the manufacture of alcohol, synthetic rubber, explosives and other materials of war.

At the end of the war the American food surplus served a more peaceful but no less important purpose. In the year ending June 30, 1947, the United States shipped to hungry and war-torn Europe 18 million long tons of food. Very little of this was corn, but the food actually sent represented, in terms of calories, the equivalent of 720 million bushels of corn. In the same year, through the use of hybrid corn, the corn crop of the United States had been increased by approximately 800 million bushels. That is, the United States' gain in this one crop was sufficient to meet Europe's food deficit during the first postwar years, with food to spare.

Hybrid corn has proved to be a catalyst affecting the entire agricultural economy wherever it has touched it. Even the most skeptical farmers, once they have proved to their own satisfaction the superiority of hybrid corn, turn to the experiment stations for other innovations growing out of agricultural research. The higher cost of hybrid seed is an inducement to strive for maximum yields, and in the United States this has led to the adoption of improved agricultural practices, including the use of fertilizers, crop rotations and the growing of soil-improving crops of soybeans and other leguminous plants that gather soil-enriching nitrogen from the atmosphere. The result of all this is that the increases in corn yields obtained by American farmers on their own farms have been much larger than in experiment stations. Whereas hybrid corn grown in controlled experiments usually yields about 20 to 30 per cent more than the original open-pollinated corn from which it derives, the average farm yield of corn per acre in the United States has increased by about 50 per cent: from about 22 bushels in the early 1930s, when hybrid corn first began to be used commercially, to approximately 33 bushels in the late 1940s, when it occupied some 75 per cent of the total corn acreage. Under favorable conditions, yields of 100 bushels per acre for hybrid corn are common, and yields exceeding 200 bushels are regularly reported. This substantial increase can be attributed to the use of fertilizers and other soil-improvement practices as well as hybrid corn.

The success of hybrid corn in the United States promises to be repeated in other parts of the world where corn is an important plant. One of the first countries to benefit is Italy, which fortunately has been able to use hybrids developed in the United States. Corn hybrids are usually so well "tailored" to a particular environment that it is seldom possible to move them successfully from one country, or even from one region, to another. Italy has proved to be an exception to this rule and is now importing hybrid seed corn from the United States on a substantial scale— enough to plant approximately a million acres in 1950.

In the countries of Latin America, in many of which corn is a basic food plant, new hybrids especially adapted to local conditions are being developed. Corn-breeding programs aimed at this objective are in progress in Mexico, Guatemala, El Salvador, Costa Rica, Cuba, Colombia, Venezuela, Brazil, Uruguay, Argentina, Peru and Chile. The corn-breeding program in Mexico, a co-operative project of the Mexican Government and the Rockefeller Foundation, has been particularly successful. Begun in 1943, it has already made itself felt in the Mexican economy; in

1948, for the first time since the Revolution of 1911, Mexico produced enough corn to feed her own population.

To Mexico hybrid corn is perhaps even more important than to the United States. In the United States three fourths of all corn is fed to livestock and is transformed into meat, milk, eggs and other animal products before reaching the ultimate consumer. In Mexico corn is used directly; it is literally the staff of life of millions of people—the daily bread, which, eaten 365 days a year, fuels most of the human metabolism. Corn has an almost sacred significance to the Mexican farmer, as it had to his ancestors for centuries past. It turns out, however, that the Mexican farmer, for all of his inherent conservatism, is, like his American counterpart, willing to try new kinds of corn.

What has been done in corn to utilize the phenomenon of hybrid vigor can be done in any crop plant that lends itself to mass hybridization. Plants of the gourd family are especially easy to hybridize. Like corn, they bear male and female flowers separately on the same plant. They are therefore easily self-pollinated to produce inbred strains and readily emasculated to effect crossing. Hybrid forms of cucumber, squash and watermelon are now grown. Like hybrid corn, they are characterized by vigor, productiveness and uniformity.

Plants in which both the male and female elements occur in the same flower present greater difficulties. In some, like the tomato, whose flower parts are relatively large and whose fruit contains a large number of seeds, hand pollinations to produce hybrid seed are feasible. In other species—such as onions and sugar beets, whose flowers are much too small and delicate to permit emasculation on a commercial scale—forms of cytoplasmic pollen sterility, similar in their effect to that described above for corn, have been used for some years. Since onions and sugar beets are grown for their vegetative parts, the problem of restoring fertility in the final hybrid is not involved. Other crop plants in which hybrid vigor is

230

either being used or tested are alfalfa, barley, rye and sorghum.

Work on the development of hybrid vigor has also been extended to domestic animals. The production of hybrid chickens has already become an enterprise second in importance only to the hybrid seed-corn industry. Hybrid pigs are coming into common use, and hybrid sheep and cattle are well along in the experimental stage. In farm animals the problem of crossing is simple, because the animals are bisexual and can reproduce only by cross-fertilization. But the problem of producing inbred strains is more difficult than in plants. Inbreeding by matings between brothers and sisters—the most intensive form possible in bisexual animals—is only one third as effective as self-pollinations in plants. Since individual animals are more valuable than individual plants, inbreeding on the vast scale on which it is practiced in plants is not yet feasible. The results so far obtained, however, have been very promising. Hybrid chickens grow faster and lay more eggs. Hybrid pigs make more pork with less feed. Hybrid cattle produce more beef in less time. The animal breeder, like the corn breeder, has found hybrid vigor a powerful force to be harnessed in raising the physiological efficiency of organisms.

The time is rapidly approaching when the majority of our cultivated plants and domestic animals will be hybrid forms. Hybrid corn has shown the way. Man has only begun to exploit the rich "gifts of hybridity."

BIBLIOGRAPHY

READERS interested in further reading on the topics covered in this book may find the list below helpful. It is *not* a bibliography of source material. The books chosen are for the most part addressed to the general reader; they include also some of the more accessible textbooks and survey volumes. The list is by no means exhaustive. Nor does it embrace the full range of interest of this book, since much of the work reported here is not yet represented in the pages of any other book. (The date given in italics under each chapter title is the date of its original publication in SCIENTIFIC AMERICAN).

THE AUXINS
May 1949
Hormones and Horticulture. George S. Avery. McGraw-Hill, 1947.
Phytohormones. F. W. Went and K. V. Thimann. Macmillan, 1937.

THE CONTROL OF FLOWERING
May 1952
"Photoperiodism in Relation to Hormones as Factors in Floral Initiation and Development." Karl C. Hamner and James Bonner in the *Botanical Gazette,* Vol. 100, No. 2; December, 1938.
Vernalization and Photoperiodism. A. E. Murneek *et al.* Chronica Botanica Co., 1948.

WHAT MAKES LEAVES FALL?
November 1955
Auxins and Plant Growth. A. C. Leopold. University of California Press, 1955.
"Studies on Abscission." R. H. Wetmore, William P. Jacobs and F. N. Rossetter in *American Journal of Botany,* Vol. 40, No. 4, pages 272-280; April, 1953. Vol. 42, No. 7, pages 594-604; July, 1955.

NEW GROWTH SUBSTANCES
April 1957
Auxins and Plant Growth. Aldo Carl Leopold. University of California Press, 1955.
"The Chemical Induction of Growth in Plant Tissue Cultures." F. C. Steward and E. M. Shantz in *The Chemistry and Mode of Action of Plant Growth Substances*. Academic Press Inc., 1956.

233

"Gibberellic Acid and Higher Plants. I: General Growth Responses." M. J. Bukovac and S. H. Wittwer in the *Quarterly Bulletin of the Michigan Agricultural Experiment Station*, Vol. 39, No. 2, pages 307-320; November, 1956.

"Isolation of Plant Growth Inhibitors from Thamnosma Montana." Edward L. Bennett and James Bonner in *American Journal of Botany*, Vol. 40, No. 1, pages 29-33; January, 1953.

"Isolation, Structure and Synthesis of Kinetin, a Substance Promoting Cell Division." Carlos O. Miller, F. Skoog, F. S. Okumura, M. H. Von Saltza and F. M. Strong in *Journal of the American Chemical Society*, Vol. 78, No. 7, pages 1,375-1,380; April 5, 1956.

"Studies on Roots. II: Effects of Coumarin, Scopoletin and Other Substances on Growth." Bruce M. Pollock, Richard H. Goodwin and Susan Greene in *American Journal of Botany*, Vol. 41, No. 6, pages 521-529; June, 1954.

CLIMATE AND AGRICULTURE

June 1957

"Ecology of Desert Plants. I: Observations on Germination in the Joshua Tree National Monument, California"; "II: The Effect of Rain and Temperature on Germination and Growth." F. W. Went in *Ecology*, Vol. 29, No. 3, pages 242-253, July, 1948; Vol. 30, No. 1, pages 1-13, January, 1949.

"Ecology of Desert Plants. III: Development of Plants in the Death Valley National Monument, California." F. W. Went and M. Westergaard in *Ecology*, Vol. 30, No. 1, pages 26-38; January, 1949.

THE GROWTH OF MUSHROOMS

May 1956

Comparative Morphology and Biology of the Fungi, Mycetozoa, and Bacteria. Anton de Bary. Oxford University Press, 1887.

"The Mushroom." C. T. Ingold in *New Biology* No. 16, pages 96-110; Penguin Books, 1955.

Mushrooms & Toadstools. John Ramsbottom. The Macmillan Company, 1953.

LEAF SHAPE

October 1949

"Youth, Old Age, and Leaf Shape in Plants. Studies in the Morphogenesis of Leaves." E. Ashby in *New Phytologist*, Vol. 47, pages 153-195; 1948.

TISSUE CULTURES

March 1950

A *Handbook of Plant Tissue Culture*. Philip R. White. The J. Cattell Press, 1943.

PROGRESS IN PHOTOSYNTHESIS

November 1953

Photosynthesis and Related Processes. Eugene I. Rabinowitch. Interscience Publishers, Inc., 1945.

Photosynthesis and Related Processes. Vol. II, Part 1. Eugene I. Rabinowitch. Interscience Publishers, Inc., 1951.

Photosynthesis. Walter Stiles. Longmans, Green, 1925.

Photosynthesis. Herman Spoehr. American Chemical Society Monograph Series, 1926.

AUTUMN COLORS

October 1950

"The Biogenesis of the Anthocyanins, I and II." Kenneth V. Thimann and Yvette H. Edmondson in *Archives of Biochemistry*, Vol. 22, No. 1, pages 33-53, May, 1949; Vol. 25, No. 1, pages 79-90, January, 1950.

PLANT MOVEMENTS

February 1955

The Carnivorous Plants. Francis Ernest Lloyd. Chronica Botanica Co., 1942.

"Leaf Movements in Mimosa Pudica." L. Marvin Weintraub in *New Phytologist*, Vol. 50, No. 3, pages 357-382; January, 1952.

The Power of Movement in Plants. Charles Darwin. D. Appleton and Company, 1898.

THE RISE OF WATER IN PLANTS

October 1952

An Introduction to Plant Physiology. O. F. Curtis and Daniel G. Clark. McGraw-Hill Book Company, Inc., 1950.

STRANGLER TREES

January 1954

"Evolution, as Viewed by One Geneticist." R. Goldschmidt in *American Scientist*, Vol. 40; 1952.

235

Genetics and the Origin of Species. Theodosius Dobzhansky. Columbia University Press, 1951.

The Material Basis of Evolution. R. Goldschmidt. Yale University Press, 1940.

THE PLANTS OF KRAKATOA

September 1949

Krakatau: 1883-1933. A: Botany. W. M. Docters Van Leeuwen. E. J. Brill, 1936.

"Krakatau." Dr. Ch. E. Stehn, Dr. W. M. Docters Van Leeuwen and Dr. K. W. Dammerman. *Fourth Pacific Science Congress,* pages 1-118.

THE ECOLOGY OF DESERT PLANTS

April 1955

"Ecology of Desert Plants." F. W. Went and M. Westergaard in *Ecology,* Vol. 29, No. 3, pages 242-253; July, 1948; Vol. 30, No. 1, pages 1-13 and 26-38; January, 1949.

Vegetation and Flora of the Sonoran Desert. Forrest Shreve and Ira L. Wiggins. Carnegie Institution of Washington, 1951.

CHEMICAL SOCIOLOGY AMONG THE PLANTS

March 1949

The Study of Plant Communities. Henry J. Oosting. W. H. Freeman, 1948.

"An Inhibitor of Plant Growth from the Leaves of Encelia Farinosa." J. Bonner and R. Gray in the *American Journal of Botany,* Vol. 35, pages 52-57; 1948.

THE FERTILIZATION OF FLOWERS

June 1951

Handbook of Flower Pollination, Vols. I, II and III. Paul Knuth. Oxford University Press, 1906-1909.

"The Flower Constancy of Bees." Verne Grant in *Botanical Review,* Vol. 16, pages 379-398; 1950.

WHEAT

July 1953

The Origin, Variation, Immunity and Breeding of Cultivated Plants. Nikolai I. Vavilov. Chronica Botanica, 1951.

The Wheat Plant. John Percival. Duckworth and Company, 1921.

THE MYSTERY OF CORN
July 1950

Corn Before Columbus. Edgar Anderson. Des Moines, 1947.

"The Origin of Indian Corn and its Relatives." Paul C. Mangelsdorf and R. G. Reeves in *Texas Agricultural Experiment Station Bulletin*, No. 574; 1939.

"The Origin and Evolution of Maize." Paul C. Mangelsdorf. *Advances in Genetics*, Vol. I, pages 161-207. Academic Press, Inc., 1947.

HYBRID CORN
August 1951

Inbreeding and Outbreeding: Their Genetic and Sociological Significance. Edward M. East and Donald F. Jones. J. B. Lippincott Company, 1919.

"Corn Breeding." Frederick D. Richey in *Advances in Genetics*, Vol. III, pages 160-192. Edited by M. Demerec. Academic Press, Inc., 1950.